Chrysanthemum 2020 Literary Anthology

Chrysanthemum 2020 Literary Anthology

From the Chrysanthemum Literary Society

Goldfish Press, Seattle

Poetry
ISBN 13: 978-1-950276-00-4
ISBN 10: 1-950276-00-7

Library of Congress Catalog Card Number: 2020933140

Book Text and Cover Design by Susan Steiner
using Aparajita.

Goldfish Press is a literary press of all genres.

Goldfish Press
4545 42nd Ave. SW
Suite 211
Seattle, WA 98116

ACKNOWLEDGMENTS

This book is supported, in part, by a grant from the

Washington State Arts Commission

WASHINGTON STATE
ARTS COMMISSION

Chrysanthemum 2020 Literary Anthology

Note from the publisher:

We are not trying to make a splash. We are only one line into the ocean of verse. This is a labor of love and that means thankless labor in some cases. Still, we are genuinely happy to present your work here, because you have written it, and we are affected by it, whether you are a pro or a neophyte is unimportant. What is important is that you believe in the written word and the way it is spoken, as for untold centuries, people believed in the magic of words.

You may have made us think (heaven forbid!), chuckle, secretly envious, or even tempted to be a word thief. But your work is your work and you have made those words your own and redefined them for us, unveiling our ignorance and limitations, as we all know that words are a dangerous tool in the hands of demagogues. But words also heal, give us hope, and show the way to freedom.

The range of the work in this anthology is not maximally inclusive. But we try to encourage those with talent to go onward and those with spirit not to give up. I can think of the lyrics to two songs, "Freedom is having nothing to lose," and "It is only words, and words are all I have, to take your love away."

Now we are necessarily biased in our choices what to include in this anthology. We can only see light in the visible spectrum as it were. We can't see what the bee sees or hear what the bat hears. And as Leonard

Cohen sang, "He sank beneath your (meaning our) wisdom like a stone." Even so, we have included world-class poets in this issue as well as first timers. I hope that you don't think it is beginners' luck. Rather, I hope you continue to be nourished by your own efforts to be an individual, and that singular voice grows sharper and more distinctive without limit.

Koon Woon / Editor, Publisher

Table of Contents

Joseph Musso

The first born is the first to leave

As a school bus stops traffic, the fog refuses to roll up just yet and
drapes itself as a winter coat over the steel bones of machinery.
The presence of children is vast, an intimidation factor,
as the future of this current society is not just in the hands of the sleepy
school bus driver with divorce on her mind, but in the hands of us all.
The sweet fruity smell of wood burning in the air is as holy a presence
as the mass candles in the dungeon-like churches of my little-boy
days…
A belief I long abandoned.
And gets stuck in my throat like bread, the body of Christ.
But there will be no confession today, as the wine has disappeared, and
none is talking, none is listening.

Snow crouches behind a dubious cloud formation awaiting the go-
ahead from "God."
And school children pray the newscasts are correct, putting all their
faith in the weatherman with the nice teeth. A line of cars ten deep on
either side of the yellow bus idle impatiently, frost covering the
windows, heaters running on high, tail pipes
smoking like cigarettes, spitting out their own doomed and dismal
poetry. But—late for work again. The bus lights flash like Christmas,
but dimmer in the stubborn fog, their brilliance thwarted, much like a
child in an over-crowded classroom.

There are faces in the weather, blinking from windows, freshly brushed teeth and the strong smell of Colgate up and down the long aisle… And wetted-down hair, with one, always one, determined strand sticking up per child. A six-year-old is pushed gently across the road by the years, a hand on his back he will become accustomed to as years pass silently but deadly… He twirls suddenly at the double yellow-line, waving tiny hand at Mother, her palm pressed to bosom, water in her eyes. The first day of school terrifies who more?

Tomorrow, he takes a wife.

Lily Maltz

Painted Sheep

I used to dream each night of painted sheep
They're climbing, dancing, deep into the night
They played together throughout my nightly sleep
as honest, as open as some young children might
but now instead I dream of dying lambs
I watch them pack their bags and head to school
One keeps her hijab clean from sticky jams
Eight drop plastic straws from on a high stool
Three are arrested walking down the street
Twelve loudly say 'no ban on stolen land'
Four injured, beaten by their lover's feet
and all of this, it is done by our hand
But Lord as I lay me down to sleep
I wish I still but dreamt of painted sheep

(Lily wrote this sonnet as a 9th grader
at Hillside Student Community School in Bellevue, Washington)

Changming (Michael) Yuan

Another Prayer

Jesus my dear Lord!

Were I
Really to have an afterlife
I hope to become a wolf, or
A fir, for instance

Just to be a bit more, or even less
                    Than a human being

Changming (Michael) Yuan

In the Shadow of Socrates

Someone tells me I look like Laozi
It is the way my forehead protrudes
Or maybe it is my eyes

Someone mentions Socrates to me
Though I am not interested in his maieutics
Nor does he seem to care about my indifference

Anyway, I remain as silent as Sphinx
Or Laozi's Dao which, once articulated
In a human speech, would become totally lost

Like truth
Like wisdom
Like any authentic knowledge

While Socrates pursues his argument persistently
I move my proto being far away
From every shaped human

He enjoys arguing
I believe whatever is voiced
Will get lost in void

He upholds logic
I uphold mythicism as someone tries to bring me
Under the influence of the Greek syntax &

Cast Socrates's shadow on my thinning soul
But I shy away farther to an unknown forest, where
 I will eventually die alone

Like an old African elephant that does not want to
Disturb the progression of
A whole migratory family

Sigrun Susan Lane

The Barnacle

In a six-walled shell, white
and calcareous as a hollow tooth,
I am cemented

to the rock on my back.
At the tide change,
the operculum doors

slide open, I send my six pairs
of dark feathers to beat
like flames against the waters

to draw the ocean in
where I wait,
like a black robed monk in his cell.

Sigrun Susan Lane

The Geoduck's Song

Laugh if you will,
I am lovely to some.
A giant among clams

Have I said I love sand,
a little thick mud?
A blanket of seaweed

keeps sea gulls away.
I live for the tide,
it brings me my life.

O sweet salt, I sing
through my long rubber hose,
a neck, not a nose.

A perfect periscope,
although I am blind.
I feel the vibrato of rain.

One day I will sing
Basso Profundo
in a chorus

Of mollusks and bivalves.
We shall sing the great
Te Deum in the key of C.

James Bertolino

Gaia Spins

Just say "moss" and see
where it takes you:

to those tiny atmospheric
organs that wave above

the green pillowing
of a small planet: Sufi spinning

her galactic dream. She runs
her tongue over her lips,

and a thunderstorm drenches
the Mojave Desert. When she makes

a fist, spontaneous combustion
illuminates a mountain cave.

Now white formations
on the underside of an eagle's

wing are the syllables
of change. Forever beach crabs

will carry her portrait, and clam
siphons rise to whistle her name.

James Bertolino

Galaxy in Thrall

I speak with an uncivil tongue.
No effort, no cause for alarm.

Blister or scrape, the beauty
of skin stretched thin.

I invite her to advance
for a bruising. Be the planet.

Be the advent of the holoreal,
where nothing achieves itself

without achieving all.
Her tender kiss, my galaxy.

My eyes, her eyes, ours.
We see ourselves, where time

is an opinion. Her space
interpenetrates, while mine

is endless repetition.
Together we hold the world.

Rodger Martin

For Del Rossis Homemade Pasta

The trattoria—crossword of the nose,
Intersection of the taste, mirror
Where tongue and ear meet eye, and plates serve song
and song sings pasta. Kitchens stage three-part
syncopated feasts, as singers salad up
Big-Daddy-Oh at the bar while musicians
Swizzle picks over strings with dessert for a star.
And in the Blue Room an aristocratic carafe
Of nebbiolo *Barolo* softens light
And mysteries between lovers' words, a brush
Like a double-pawed cat curling among the tables,
Nuzzling, kneading our muzzles to a satisfied purr.

Lesby
(from the painting by NC Wyeth)

Within the dense coil of the flirt all
is light. A woman in blue offers
her breast, an arm, the bowl of sustenance,
the apron of matrimony. The man
considers. His bright day of youth like
some cumulous beyond reckoning
piles behind him.   Already he has left
the slim girl in lavender, her memory
darkening, hopes brief as her lilac halo.
What endures—his arm reaching security
in the mane of his horse, fingers gently
scratch the coarse nape while the Percheron drinks.
Its patient eyes miss nothing, muzzle deep
in cool water of spring, wise to this keep.

Joel Kabakov

Astronomy

You asked for a chocolate truffle
right after refusing my offer
of the sun, moon and stars

you responded to my lust
with the names of every bird
fidgeting through
the plum tree
outside our window.

astronomy has always
worked for you

with precision
you practice
the gravitational pull,
the invisible force
that holds fast comets to
their eccentric orbits

especially the ones that
come our way
once in a lifetime.

What if words are a substitute for silence?

In my ripening years I am
possessive of the Mystery—
no one else may own the Still, Small Voice.
Let me be an apologist for a glass of water,
for the realness contained on the back of a penny,
caught in its ridges and grooves,
copper certainty.

Do not tell me what Truth is
as though you could describe the backs of my eyelids.
Let me be a mystic of the seen.

Truth rides through the capillaries
in my brother's feet,
the white cells slowly succumbing.

Once I saw Jesus drawing in the sand,
myself a star falling to earth,
and begged him to only look at me,
implored him to call my name.

Now he is as near as my bones,
and I a vapor in the Cloud of Unknowing,
my name immaterial,
my worthiness unstrung.

When I close my eyes
I see my brother
dancing his infant son across the floor,
singing, "You'll never find
as long as you live
someone who loves you
like I do."

Clandestine

I want to sneak into the poem,
slip it into a shot glass like it's the last bit of really good whiskey.
I know I told you I don't like whiskey,
but I lied.
One sip of the good stuff goes down like love on the kitchen floor at
three AM.

It's been too long a while.
Didn't expect to break out the stilettos,
but didn't plan on being naked, either.
One seductive simile begs another
and another—
a little death.

I light a cigarette in the afterglow.
Whatever hangover comes banging on my door
is worth
every
drop.

David Mason

Remembering the Year of the Tiger

The other day I ran across an old lens cloth with the address of
Meishido Optician, Sasebo, Japan, printed on it. Out of curiosity I
googled it and was directed to a website where to my surprise I could
access the 1962 yearbook of the Ernest J. King Military Dependent
School. The Sasebo optician was one of the sponsors of E.J. King's
yearbooks. I spent my freshman high school year there in 1962 as a
Navy brat.

At the end of WWII, the US Navy took over most of the Sasebo
Imperial Japanese Naval Base. The school was located in a building
that reputably had been the command post where the Pearl Harbor
bombing was planned. In any case the order to the Imperial Japanese
Fleet to proceed with the attack was sent by Hario Radio towers, which
still stand 15 miles outside of Sasebo.

Directly across the smelly Sasebo River from the school was a densely
packed bar district that catered to the needs of young American sailors
on shore leave. Especially popular were Bar and Paradise Alleys, as
well as the Kasbah Night Club. From one of my classrooms I could see
the Bar Blonde across the water. Walking to school or home,
occasionally I would be propositioned by a face powdered lady
standing at a bar door stoop with the words, "Huba huba baby san." It
took me a while to understand what she had in mind.

Betty, our Japanese maid, always knew when a big aircraft carrier was scheduled to make a port of call. On such days she would leave work early, but not before getting all dolled up. Hours later her husband would drop by with a worried demeanor. We would tell him, "Betty go sayonara."

Looking through the yearbook I found a dedication to my mathematics teacher, Mr. Harry Herbert Eller. It was noted that he had attended West Point and had served in Europe in WWll attaining the rank of LT Colonel in the Army Airforce. Since leaving the Airforce he had taught at four military service schools around the world. From what I remember of my teachers it is my impression that such overseas employment was an avenue for misfits with modest means to see the world.

Mr. Eller was the high school teacher that had the most influence on my future direction. He had a rather unique way of running his classes. He occupied two adjoining classrooms, whose walls were lined with blackboards. He did very little lecturing. Instead every student was required to stand at a board and work his or her way through the exercises in the textbook at his or her own pace, as Mr. Eller walked around observing progress giving help when needed. Students were expected to come in early or stay late to do extra work. He divided the class into three groups according to achievement and ability. These were the A, B and C groups. The letters signified the highest grade that a person in his or her assigned group could earn. Of course based on progress movement from one group to another was possible. If Mr. Eller caught a student loafing off, the poor boy or girl received the full force of a Dr. Eller tirade. In fact from time to time the school principal would call on Mr. Eller's fearsome presence to re-establish decorum when things got rowdy in the gym.

The dedication writes: Mr. Eller believes that students should work according to their abilities. Because of this factor, the mathematical genius may inquire into new fields, while the slower student advances at a pace tuned to his understanding. Every student feels that he can ask for extra help at any time because this teacher works before to late after school for the benefit of his students.

Mr. Eller was impressed when I brought to class my father's midshipman school spherical trigonometry textbook. I managed to teach myself elementary calculus while at E.J. King. Much later I developed into a research mathematician and university professor, very likely due to stern Mr. Eller's early impetus. Mr. Eller was a tiger and, by coincidence, 1962 was the year of the Tiger.

Luis Cuauhtemoc Berriozabal

LOOKING AT THE SEA

Looking at the sea
I feel a tremble
as a tide of sorrow
washes over me. It
lasts for a moment
as the sorrow ends.

Feeling drowsy, I
watch the waves and I
close my eyes. I see
her in a doorway.
She is just a ghost
smelling of the sea.

Luis Cuauhtemoc Berriozabal

LET NIGHT BREATHE

What could I
do, but to
let night breathe?
There could be
one more night,

a thousand
more; routes
to the sea,
drunken nights
and the light. A
blind man sees
what others
cannot see.
Avoid the
shiny stars
and full moon.
Let silence

in and feel
it deep where
your pulse beats.

A PROTEST POEM ABOUT PROTEST POEMS
(in 9 parts)

1.

Mainly because they don't work.

They have the shelf-life of a mayfly.

If a protest poem in the last 60 years

had been effective,

my 23 year-old daughter

would know who Nixon was.

2.

There is an expression in stand-up comedy, "Playing to the band."

It means addressing an audience already sympathetic to your

viewpoint.

A multitude of sub-genres exist for the protest poet:

The MFA protest poem read at the local bookstore

which usually begins with the poet watching the news in the breakfast

nook

and having to confront the atrocities of the world and their own

privilege,

being sure to employ the Seven Types of Ambiguity,

while folks sit in folding chairs and nibble on wine & brie.

Sometimes they shed a tear and get

the stone-ground whole grain crackers soggy.

The slam poet whose rapid-fire agitprop delivered
to an audience of fellow travelers has to get at least
a dozen mini-ovations in 3 minutes in order to advance
to the finals and maybe even get in a Nike ad or a movie
like Saul Williams, who lives in Paris now.

The viral poets who get a million hits because
their protest poem somehow involves a Marvel comics superhero
and be all like "Wow, I'm CHANGING THE WORLD!"
Publishers used to give them book deals
until they discovered the hard way
no one who reads something for free on their phone
is gonna shell out $15.95

Gutter-snipe street poets who gather in low dives and
chant diatribes of nihilistic rage and despair and bleak jokes
only to forget what they read the next morning.
I like this last group the best, but they are being driven out
of our big cites by the economic Darwinism
that is making them choose between beer or rent.

3.
This manifesto does not apply to protest songs.
Protest songs have a beat that people can march to.
Even Pete Seeger singing all 843 verses of "We Shall Overcome",
mind-numbingly boring as it is,
covers a lot of ground in 4/4 time.
Mao would have been proud.

4.

In 2003, the late Sam Hamill (Buddha rest his soul)
started an organization called "Poets Against the War"
which hosted events nationwide where local bards
read their poems protesting the Iraq War.
A couple years back on Facebook, Sam, in ailing health,
was bemoaning the fact that he couldn't find
a suitable institution (Yale, the Smithsonian, the Library of Congress,
Turlock Community College) willing to house
a complete archive of these works for time immemorial, which by that
time
consisted of – what for it – 20,000 POEMS.
Seriously? In our desperate desire to preserve at least a fraction
of our culture for future generations before the coming apocalypse,
one would think it might be necessary to prioritize.
I pity the archaeologist from across the galaxy (probably an intern)
whose job is to plow through all these in an effort
to find out where our civilization went wrong.

"So, QUISP 7-1128, how do you conjecture
this ancient race went extinct?"

"Well, sir, apparently they were ALL POETS."

5.

The actual print anthology of "Poets Against the War", however,
(for those with long memories) was pared down to 150 entries.
Does anyone besides the poets who are in it and
their closest immediate loved ones even have a copy of this?

And some of those folks must have died, because
I see stray copies in used bookstores, where they will
no doubt sit until the wrecking ball converts
their brick & mortar home to new condos.
6.
Not that this phenomenon is limited to protest poetry.
It's true of every bloody anthology ever published,
with the exception of frigging "When I Grow Old, I Shall Wear
Purple."
Pro-tip: the only reason to be in a poetry anthology
is for the off-chance that some Really Famous Poet is in it,
so you can say "I'm in a book with *insert name here*
and thus give the false impression that
you are somebody, too.

7.
On the other hand, Sam Hamill's book of translations
"Only Companion: Japanese Poems of Love and Longing"
will last as long as English is spoken.

8.
Is "The Second Coming" a protest poem?
If so, I'll have to rethink the entire issue.

9.
In conclusion, although now we can all agree that
protest poems suck and are the work of whiny milksops,
poems about actual revolutions are WAY COOL.
William Blake's "The French Revolution",

Mayakovsky's odes to his Bolshevik comrades,
Diane Di prima's "Revolutionary Letters",
Johnny Horton's "The Battle of New Orleans"—
These aren't just poems, they're
Instruction Manuals for Whoop-Ass.
Because the only thing these people understand
is the WHIP.
Or, in the words of Teddy Roosevelt,
"Free versely, and carry a big stick.
and HIT the bastards with it,
and KEEP hitting them until
they beg for mercy.
And then, hit them some more…"

Mike Dillon

Insomnia

All night I listened to the rain drum
my swaybacked roof and eaves.

Dawn brings the promise of a bright
disc of risen sun.

And an overwhelming question:
When, exactly, in last night's rain

did the first pink camellia flower open?

Mike Dillon

August

A white bowl waits on the kitchen counter
for a few chosen friends to arrive so we can
set out to my secret blackberry patch.
The thick, 19th century novel I've been reading,
fresh as this morning's dew, waits on the table
for when I get to be alone again in the afternoon.
But now's the time, while I'm waiting,
to put on that classic, syrupy record I love.
I'm sure I know better but I don't care.

Time to slow dance solo before the stone
fireplace where the kindling I laid
after May's final fire is ready for late September.
The foghorn has quit its bovine lowing.
Gauzy sunlight, after finding the orchard,
filters through the cedar to the old fir floor.
Time is lenient now.
I close my eyes and slow-step to the music,
the heart no longer pretending.

Joanna Conom

For Henry (inspired by Margaret)

I remember my silver dollars
   Stolen long ago
Earned when we were strong scented girls
   flushed fresh with new bodies
   such an adventure being new
My eyes are like yours now
   filmed and faded
   focused on memory
Your garden was full with spring
   Do we like pink silk slips?
   sit down then
Cheap rubber slippers fell
   you rubbed our feet
   slowly and of unknown purpose
We lured quiet with tales
   of long ago
   and fancy things
Rewarded each with a silver dollar
We were strong scented girls
   who knew to run fast
   when handed money
Only to return again
   Asking for our pink silk slips

Joanna Conom

recipe for proper lentils

a little wilted
too long chilled
without all the leftover things
the soup is incomplete
spice past sell by date
smells like beans
dried tomatoes from
five Christmases ago
last herbs from outdoor pots
cauldron of hope
mix ginger root with onion
paint yourself
with red lipstick
close the curtains
turn on the fire
mix it all up
hold back the night
garnish with lemon zest
and stars

Sandra Noel

Driving home after your cancer diagnosis

In comfortable conversation
Sparked by the usual strife
We infuse
Being who we are.
We are closer to the end
Of our days.
Not much has changed
And everything.

We were never hand holders
Or dancers in the dark
But I remember when
We were in Wadaura, Japan
Your blue eyes
The color of the sea
And I was thinking, OK, this is it.

There were no bells ringing
Or the music I'd imagined
Just the sigh of the sea
Flowing off the jetty rocks
And back again.
I was standing ankle deep
In blood from the last whale
Dragged up and flensed down

On the concrete platform
The great eastern sun
Resting on the horizon
Your eyes the color
Of the sea.

Sandra Noel

Star craft

Chafing the lines little by little
There is no rudder or sail
On her own my craft is crafty
Bent on open water
And something indefinable
Behind the stars.

The wind is calm
And the bay a mirror
For the moon
When the heron calls me awake
I light the candles
Ring the bowl
Find my seat.

Stillness carries its own wind
Rustling through my thoughts
Loosening the moorings

Sandra Noel

Your river is not mine

But shines under the same moon
The only connection
All other ties are sliced at their roots
A harvest of memories that feed no one
Unless we live on light.

If only this were possible
To drink in the moon like milk
Wade into the water
Of a river to the north
A river to the south
Both leading to the sea.

Margaret Roncone

(untitled)

At the edge of the woods
I hang my apron in a low
branch of cedar
when I return to
early morning tasks
I will rub bird smudge
from the pockets
shake baby bees
from the crinkled ties.

Cedar

It is said they are
guardian of bones
small insects weather-wiped clean
of body form
why is my intimacy with
crisp fern foiled by winter's
breath so vital to me?
So I file through
the backwoods of my brain
a one person search party
crawling through rusty leaves
and soil.

Margaret Roncone

I fall in love with a photo of e. e. cummings in a New Yorker Magazine while in the waiting room of an ophthalmologist's office

it's black and white
he's looking intently
away from the camera at
a parade of lower case 'i's
a hyphened world
linear time and rhyme
disappear in a desert
of white stallions
my eyes balloon
at handsome
I need to nestle in his
supra sternal notch
feel his swallows
as they gather
on telephone wires
stretched
from limb
to beautiful
limb.

Leopoldo Seguel

Saving Grace

do you not love this land
down blooming cottonwoods
down dirt paths further on
down rivers, lakes, and foggy swamps

where dreamy fishermen troll
where bottom feeders swim deep
where cattails conceal the red-wing black bird

singing morning noon and night
singing dusk and dawn
singing swooping songs and trills

till everything turns inside out
till my heart feels warm about
till ears sweet shrilling buzzing

eyes glazed hypnotic chanting
praying all night long, all night long
for rain and saving grace

Leopoldo Seguel

Drifting

drifting in the hammock of night
sweet air cradles you and me
under the tropic of Capricorn

as moonlight shines on the water
we are foreigners to paradise
even the birds sing strangely

our longing does not fade with sunset
nor does it still our desire, now forgotten
until we bear again the pain of leaving

we fall through deep space to Jupiter
the stars and far beyond the end of time
and track our lives with telescopes

make markings on scraps of paper
we stuff deep into our pockets
to read at home by firelight

S.P. Clarke

Sky

I would give you birds
  to prove my love,
    if there were but enough birds
  in all the sky above.
I would write words
  to show me true,
    if there were such words
I could craft for you.
But, only the silence
  of a breeze
    whispered among
  the branches of trees
    can but suggest
  what you, in your heart
    and soul, know best.
This love we share
  is as endless as air;
    as timeless as a sigh;
  as sweet
    as it is rare—
Yet, more plentiful
    than even birds
  in the sky.

Link

Oh, engine my future,
  my darling motor spark.
And angel still my heart
  with a flaunt
    of your flawless wings.
I awe stand stark
  in the silent dark,
    beneath your brilliant lightning shadow.
A diamond destiny compiled
  from the dust of all things.
In mute, our screaming lives
  share a desperate quiet link—
    to be less
      than we may believe,
    yet far more
  than we might think.

Joneve McCormick

Meditations

Ethics is the practice of optimum survival. I can seek escape by going out the bottom but only find freedom in looking, willing to see.

There's no reason to punish myself for whatever used to be. I choose ongoing to play my part — that's my point being in the drama. The more complete my view, the better fit the parts.

We create our worlds or God creates through us; there is no separation; we are one. But as mortals as well we have to choose between good and evil; tragically, at times between two or more goods vitally important.

Everything is permitted.

Mary Anna Kruch

What the Tourists Miss

I. In the Vineyards

From a distance, smoke drifts
across the valley from Paradise,
an ironic name for a town
burned to the ground.
It is magic hour in Napa,
and the rerouted Wine Train slows
to a snail's pace for photographs.
Late afternoon shadows
grow tall in vineyards still standing,
and the sky hints at lavender.
The boss is there among the grapes,
pausing to mop his forehead
before calling in his workers
for the day.
Out there since 4 AM,
all are more than ready
to head home to family.
Gas masks are peeled off,
thrown into the beds of pick-ups –
until tomorrow
when another smoky 12-hour day begins.

II. At the Tree Farm

The mountain is still scorched;
Sauvignon Blanc and Chardonnay
vines stand spindly in spots,
distressed by October's fires
up and down the valley.
On this December day,
the tree farm's open for business
in front of spaces where chimneys
and concrete slabs remain
for the family who work the place;
a run-down trailer with Christmas lights
stands bravely in a clearing.
This year's three days of rain
brought timid, new blades of grass —
but most are gone,
ravaged by thin, famished cattle
on nearby slopes.
Fortunately, when flames jumped the highway,
the tallest, grandest trees were spared.
Price tags on fresh-cut
Douglas Firs and Scotch Pines
shock the tourists.
They leave empty-handed,
crack open a $195 bottle
of Cabernet Sauvignon,
head back to their hotels.

J. Edward Moss

THESE STREETS ARE BATHED IN SHADOW
(Rochester)

yes, i'll admit
i ate the sun raw
no sugar
no salt no pepper

no rise no set
       just as is
              where it sat
amongst the cosmos.

sure our planet suffered
but, i was fed up.
shiny bastard always startin' a fuss
so damn early each day.

so yes,
       darkness all the time
       was a choice
i had to make
in the night
       i am level
       and clear
in the night
       i am without
       nudity
i am cloaked
with clarity

so i chose to keep us all in the dark.

John Burgess

THESE STREETS ARE BATHED IN SHADOW
(Seattle)

We spend our days under cover
of gray like wet cement
leaves us in a druggy fog
where matters aren't that set

wrapped in strips of musty linen
there's if things have ended

we stumble thru nothingness
our view of no distinction here
no discerning sky from street no
telling
heaven hidden.

Untitled by Liam Roche 2018

I am not the soldier.
I am the battlefield, the spoils—the purpose of divine war.

Untitled by Liam Roche 2018

The sun holds back no brilliance and the day is cold despite this.
The boy waits for the girl while he sits at the center of the diner filling
with morning.
The waiting is ancillary.
Among the few others there murmuring, he hears other murmurings
which rise and fall, searching for opportunities to harmonize.

And clouds do pass too and fill the room and the street and the city
with the tension of shadows in a slow-motion siren of light.
It is on this stage the coffee steam rises and creeps, the silverware
clatters and the Formica sparkles with its own stars in a frozen green
universe.
He is gone into it.

The girl, a few blocks away, wonders if this boy could be trained to be
something else—to lose his strangeness,
to be like other boys,
to have his handsomeness made thorough.
She is imagining embracing him in ways that wake him

from his dreams.
At first, the boy is not thinking of her; he is losing himself in another
moment in which everything speaks.

And then, he also sees the two of them embracing
while the checkered tile floor and the green counter top and everything
in the universe vibrates as voices of angels,
and all light is overcome, and he holds her tight not out of simple love,
but to keep God from falling out of her.

Appeal by Liam Roche 1991

Peace, come gently.
Ease the door in both soft hands.
For a change
gather caution and regard
when you walk to my bed.
Don't dump your clothes on the hardwood.
Fold and place like woven crystal,
Then lie down with me.

Untitled by Liam Roche 2019

I am given to the world
to see the world.
To be destroyed by the world.

Wendy Beamish

What is Done is Done

Remember that day when the Earth,
Violently flipped inside out,
And the crows flew scrapping
Against the sky,
Before it righted itself.

On that day,
As I stood surveying
The Shattering of Souls,
Knowing that my life
Could not be the same again,
Staring down at the dead crow
That had fallen to my feet,

On that day,
As I stood,
On this gutted, empty shell
Of landscape
I understood that
The only way now was
Forward.

Sensing the dented sky
Softly convulse,
I reached up
And gently pushed

Its arc
Closer to the stars.

Act V

The time is coming
When I will no longer
Be able
To reach the fruit on the vine

When I am no longer
Able to press the
Sweet fruit
To my lips.
I will become a crazed animal
Violently thrashing,
 Remembering

That once the
Ripe, succulent fruit
Was so easy to reach.
 And each day
The world
Would present me
With a brilliant array of
Opportunities that I
 Would carefully pick

But now,
The heavy curtains

Draw closer
And laden with their weight
I see the days grow shorter.

And in my glorious greed,
While there is still time,
I will indulge in the spoils
That fall from the vine.

Lyn Coffin

Gender

(The Box of Broken Toys)

He stretches on the rooted ground beneath a birch
and puts the box of broken toys between her knees.
A naked doll with one arm gone
displays a plastic smile with confidence
amid a wrecker's paradise of matchbox cars....
Just yesterday, s/he finally came to visit,
and after a defrosted dinner, the three of them faced off across
a scarred and varnished table to discuss
the parents' need to move. And then (s/he's thought this out)
while s/he retired to the attic and lay sleepless,
sweating on the covers of a short and narrow bed,
his father died (as they say) peacefully in sleep;
her mother must have come awake to find her husband gone
and did not summon help but lay there stubborn,
demanding that her Christian god should take her, too....
So she or he, their one adulted child
came down the crooked stairs this morning,
to find them lying nearly straight beside each other—
colder, stiffer, than in life— a knife and spoon laid out for dinner....
Cell phone calls between white mugs of bitter coffee
have set the wheels to funeral in motion....
The parents presupposed the genders s/he was heir to,
the one born into and the one assumed,
but now the parents' deaths reduce all gender

to a child's neutrality. It's just a child who
reaches in the box and raises up the doll,
finds tiny clothing in a metal tin for bandages,
and manages to deck that sexless plastic body for a funeral
in dress and hat and heels. It's just a child,
the only living person present at the scene .

Lyn Coffin

Veils of Water: The 8 Decades of Her Life

she caught minnows in her hands— they died
trying to breathe through a veil of air

a stranded child wades toward a woman
she sees as a veiled moon cut in quarters

she meets a boy who lives in his body
with one wet finger he punctures her veil

she kills her insides like a sleepwalking actor
shredding red veils into swirled-away water

a man comes pushing through veil after veil
he moves and she turns a tide in her rising

she drapes a black veil over her bed
she cries for weeks and covers the windows

she disrobes in a room under a cross
her breath is frost veiling the windows

she stands beside God on the bank of a river
and sheds her body like a veil into water

Bob Moore

Beyond Words

And what to make of living whys—
the shapes of things, a black-winged bird,
a woman with a pair of eyes
that speaks without a single word,

a cell that knows what time to split,
what form to take. Its work creates
a being with a space that's fit.
But why it differentiates

or knows how best to use the sun,
or lives along the forest floor,
or leaves its birthright when it's done,
and give no explanation for

its striving in its own defense,
is like a riddle in suspense.

Bob Moore

This Morning

I'm listening to the work of bees,
listening to the songs of birds.

I'm watching a swallowtail land,
and wing its way from bloom to bloom
in a stand of goldenrod.

The wind is bending read canary grass,
purple thistle, lambsquarters,
and Queen Anne's lace.

The ocean waves create a sound
that echoes against a barrier of boulders.

Two men at a distance from the coast
cast their lines in an open boat.

A woman in a kayak oars
her way toward shore.

Two dogs take turns running into the ocean
to wet their coats.

This morning you'd never know
there was anything but a

reverberation of peace
in the air and on the ground.

Diana Elser

My Contribution to the War

Utapao is a Thai navy base on the Gulf of Thailand,s used by the USAF
during the VietNam War to stage reconnaissance flights and bombing
raids over Viet Nam.

Loaded with towels, toys, books, and water
I tell my three-year old daughter
we're going to the beach.
We take the baht bus to the airbase,
then the base bus to the beach. We walk a long time,
from a chain-linked boundary by a guard tower,
to a barbed-wire fence by a sewage outlet, and back.

Midway, we settle on our bamboo mats
near the snack shack, runways behind us, warm ocean in front.
We race the waves, collect shells, shovel sand
into cans and buckets until the B-52's begin take-off,
one by one, over the gulf and east
following orders.

My daughter curls under me, face scrunched
stuffed animal clutched
between elbows, fingers in her ears.
Spit rattles under our tongues as the planes
and their frantic shadows clear the beach,
vibrate bones and flesh.
Other mothers hold their children, cover ears,

huddle underground if they can, dreading
not plane engine noise, but the fisted slam
of bombs by the hundreds blowing
everyone, everything apart.

Our ears did not bleed.
Their night cries were not my daughter's, not my own.

Diana Elser

Broken Chord

What joyful tones were friend and family
to the labored soul whose fingers plucked

harpstrings , counterweight to life, cantilevered
off a bridge, the ground below

somehow calling in its keenest musical key
for sacrifice.

Sounded like practice, like peace
to the bent ear, the fibrillated heart

wanting only to abandon
its useless container, wild with vibrato

mind running too hot-too cold,
yearning to be wise, to believe,

mind unable to think its way home,
or to one more minute — only caesura,

so chooses the fall — a fluttering arpeggio
octave by octave, hand over hand.

Marjorie Sadin

First Date

A blind date, I had ginger tea. You had coffee, black.
I took a nap before, and almost overslept.

When we got to my place, I invited you to come up.
I didn't usually let men come up.

We were nervous.
You said your wife had died.
I had been hospitalized.

You weren't a musician, an artist or a poet.
But you surprised me. Your kiss, the lavender roses.
You were shy as a hummingbird.

I remember that date the same way I remember
how my mother drove me home from the hospital
in a blinding snowstorm.

Marjorie Sadin

Fire

Wood crackles like an old man's voice.
Flames leap like acrobats.

I warm my wet socks
and hands in the fire.

My thoughts go to times
when our bodies warmed each other.

Your old letters shrivel in the fire
I burn to keep the blaze alive.

The poker stirs memories.
Sparks like fireflies in a summer night.

If you were here,
I wouldn't need the fire.

Lewton Thomas Jones

July Came by and gave August all her Gold

July came by and gave August all her gold
Love glimmers in her shadow
Skylarks sing to her sunlit flaxen air
Time rides a butterfly backwards
Upon the warm Summer of imagination
Trees sway in the honeyed blue heat
Lemon sunflowers wave
Lime spaded bowers clap
Long heated limbs & wheat tips
Twirl in the arid wind lilt
Bright solar light shards spray the fields
July exits as beautiful as a dove
August arrives like a golden stream
I watched beauty cross the narrow fields of Summer
A woman kissed by air and water
The soft touch of a harvest beckoned
Ecstatic to waltz the infinite.

Lewton Thomas Jones

On the Other Side of Here is a Blue Pool

On the other side of here is a blue pool
Afternoons they serve iced tea and coke
A Brentwood fantasy in Mulholland land
Pepper trees and grapefruit bees await us
Perfumed intoxication ala the Santa Ana wind
We awake, pluck oranges in the chlorine heat
Fences and palm trees protect us
Water waivers waist high as dragons fly by
A witness protection paradise
She writes letters till I arrive
A Shannon river diary
Far from the weeping
L.A Music Biz Buzz
Artificial like Vegas
A place called Progress
Right next to Boring
On the other side of here
Is a blue pool.

Sonetos de Cascadia 6.5.2019

"The people walk as if in a movie dream
And work in the terrifying order
Of a chaos their bodies reject…"

- Philip Lamantia - "A Simple Answer to the Enemy"

"You love the maps.
Tho they lied
they got you here."

- Diane di Prima, "Cartography"

For Mary Norbert Körte

The Cascadia map starts at Willets where you went, Sister Mary, to
employ the common planetary mission of mutual respect & ended up
just this side of chaining yourself to a redwood to stop the saw—
wielding ancient tree murderers as if a redwood could be a giant
version of a Catholic scapular, as if Julia Butterfly Hill's a martyr.
Maybe the martyr's Luna the redwood. We enter the gates "here at the
edge/of our journey… learn the spring with blind fingers" ripping the
filter off a cigarette before lighting another one in grief for a tradition
picked the material over values we might call *human* learning to hear
"the smoke of many voices." Here we are Sister Mary, thrashing about
"in the coffin of that green country" knowing mountains may not

survive as Nanao Sakaki knew twisting Tu Fu for our post-modern era (empire in death throes) while we watch with you, become with you "the water and the flood [that] easter forth the day" to put technology & man-made intelligence behind every echo of your blossoming "luminous awe."

7:36am - 6.5.2019

All quotes from Mary Norbert Körte

Paul Nelson

Sonetos de Cascadia 4.23.2019

You follow the teachings // yet still can't distinguish those
                                        wild flowers in your
heart.

- Zhang Er - Secret Words

If we can't get along then who the fuck can?

- Bernadette Mayer - Sonnet: Kamikaze

Another Sonnet For Ma
(Gringos Discover Avocado)

Ma needed another sonnet & Mackey says something more than 14
lines
& Kozer calls a poet whose work he hates "sophomorish" & I don't
have
the heart to correct him, but will certainly not feed him chicharrones
though gringos have apparently discovered them soon after discovering
avocado for their millennial toast. I didn't need to discover
ampersands, little "Celtic knots" Cole Swenson says of Brenda Hillman
in Lana Turner & is it love that dies w/ every unkind gesture or lives w/
every flower foto on Instagram? Yes to publishing books described in
reviews in the coastal weekly as "meaty." Yes to intention, of each act,
even flossing as Allen told me he did "exactly" after miso soup w/

69

squash & leaks (I believe) w/o checking the text of Autumn Leaves w/o
questioning his penchant for pederasty. Maybe all those candles Ma lit
did sink into me somehow & it wasn't just the Latihan, rabbits & blood
draws the little 70s toy drinking bird bobbing in a water glass growing
yet another attempted avocado tree.
8:21am - 4.23.20

Joseph Musso

IMMACULATE

My sister arrived with Jesus in her pocket. Her husband, a large man,
dwarfed the six-foot cross in his arms. There were commandments on
their breath. And recruitment on their minds.

When they first drove up in his dead father's car, he honked and waved
a hand through the window. Grinning. Black wrap-around sunglasses.
The cross lashed to the roof like a surfboard.

In the weeks before they arrived, I'd been wandering around, taking
long sandaled walks through the desert of the beach, as waves crashed,
and the sun rose and fell. I was curious by nature, but I needed fact.

I believed in what fit in my hands, what moved, what made a sound. I
was a detective looking for evidence. I looked for robes, shrouds, bits
of wood from a shipwreck, small puddles of blood beneath hands and
feet. I wanted to find love and truth and live in the place I found them.
The questions were simple ones. What is life? What is death? Why am
I here?

It was more than that. It was less. Whose black book of murder is this?
Whose rules are we following? When I was five or six my mother
began to teach me all she knew about God. My father reinforced this.
Be kind to people, they said. Help others.

My sister's husband challenged me to a fight. "What I mean," he said, "is I will play you in chess for your Belief." He grinned and I thought I saw a gold tooth. When I asked, he smiled for me and my observation was confirmed. The tooth twinkled in the sunlight. At night, no doubt it would light their way home. Its sale of course would feed many. "I am a man of my word," he said. "And I give you my word I would never take from the poor."

"Are you trying to sell me a car?"

"She's a beaut!"

The chessboard was set up. There were drinks, wine in goblets. Hors d'oeuvres served in the form of small wafers. My sister was giving birth in the corner to a ten-pound Doubt.

My sister screamed about me, "He'll never agree to it! He won't!" She screamed this while heaving, pushing, grunting, expelling the throbbing mass from her body. "I grew up with him! I know him! There will never be God in his heart!"

"Nancy Reagan," I said quietly to her, "is not your mother."

"You never stop grinning," I told her husband.

"It's the surgery," he said. "Christians must never show doubt."

As I was setting up the chessboard, I asked him, "You want the Black pieces or the White ones?"

"Oh the Whites, the Whites! The Blacks are harder to control," he said.

"So, what's the bet again?" I asked.

"If I win, you will Believe."

"What if I win?" I asked.

"Then you won't believe."

I stared at him. I counted his perfect teeth. He had more than his allotment. It worried me. What other tricks did he have up his sleeve? What other human items did he have in surplus and was hiding? What other decks were stacked against me? Would he be able to cheat without me seeing? Would he lull me into a false state of serenity and then steal my soul? Would there be frogs soon to distract me?

"What do you mean by Belief?" I asked.

"I mean if I win, then your heart belongs to Jesus."

"And if I win," I said, "then your dead father's car belongs to me."

"Deal!"

The first move was his. Pawn, one space forward. My sister stood and moved in place.

Michael G. Hickey

Watching Pain Dry

worst class ever their was too much reading. class was boring. i think i would rather watch pain dry than be in that class. the only good thing is he didnt keep us for the full two hr require.

— online teacher/course evaluation published anonymously by college student in Texas

Dear Anonymous,

I regret you thought my class was boring, and there was too much reading. Since it was a literature course I'm not sure what you were expecting, but I apologize for failing to meet your academic standards. Inasmuch as grades have already been submitted, I'm afraid it's too late to receive a tuition reimbursement, but I feel obliged to share my teaching philosophy.

In 1972, I returned from my second tour of duty in Vietnam. For months I had dreams in which I was trying to kill Charlie with my bayonet, but it took forever. I had dreams about my friend Logan who got his face shot off. I also had dreams about the little boy I killed because I thought he was carrying a grenade. (It was actually a toy soldier.) Psychologists used to call my condition *battle fatigue* or being *shell-shocked*. Today they refer to it as *post-traumatic stress*. All I knew back then was that there was a movie projector in my head and no matter how hard I tried I couldn't turn it off. I used to tap my foot uncontrollably and drink a bottle of 100 proof scotch to get to sleep. I'd

74

wake up screaming my mother's name. I'd wake up screaming *kill, kill, kill.* If you watch movies and see anything resembling glory, don't be fooled. It's all a fabrication. In Nam, death was as commonplace as life. I once saw a man step on a land mine and get blown up into a bamboo grove. He was still alive and blinking his eyes even though he had no lower torso.

Alcohol, sleeping pills, and despair became so prevalent that I used to take solace in contemplating suicide. There was a voice in my head saying *you're a pussy, you're a goddamn coward, you don't have the guts to do it, be a man, for once in your life be a man and pull the trigger...* I held a gun to my left temple and stared in the mirror every morning for 97 days in a row. The cool metal barrel was welcome relief against the concentration of body heat. Nietzsche was wrong. That which did not kill me did not make me stronger; it only made me hate being alive.

Then one morning (and don't ask me how), I woke up and said, *I think I want to live.* Imagine that. My Uncle Nicky got me a job on the railroad, and I started going to night school. I developed an insatiable appetite for reading: Americans, Russians, Brits... anything I could get my hands on. I started writing, too. And in time, no longer did I punch holes in walls or kick in doors. The facial twitching subsided and the auditory hallucinations waned. No longer was my head on a swivel. But guilt and shame are still a part of me. I killed a lot of people. I killed a little boy holding a toy soldier. The date is tattooed on my left wrist, May 25, 1970. It just so happens that was Memorial Day but of course for me, every day is Memorial Day. So you see, I, too, have watched pain dry. It is a slow and methodical process to be sure, which is why I sometimes felt the need to dismiss class early.

In conclusion, I apologize for the distress I have caused you. I understand how challenging my class must have been because even today, I sometimes ask myself if all of this is real or just a vivid, virulent dream.

Respectfully,
Professor Grayson

Jimmy Pappas

No Comfort is There in the Sound of Wind

No comfort is there in the sound of wind
in August, time of summer surplus, when
the blue phlox blooms in wooden flowerpots
beside the door that always stays unlocked.

No comfort is there in a sudden cold
which slips in unexpectedly and fools
the caterpillar into thinking that
it's time to sleep within its warm cocoon.

No comfort is there in a bitter chill
that creeps in through the window screens and makes
the woman pull her collar tight and sit
and gaze in silence at the orange sun.

Jimmy Pappas

The Football Field

The seagulls scatter across the football field;
fine dining comes in many different forms.

The autumn leaves are a mixture of red, yellow, and green;
my feelings are difficult to express in a few words.

Tiny white worms hang by threads from the elms
while I smile without speaking at the passing stranger.

The blue and white goalposts point upward,
so many of my dreams have not yet come true.

I search through the blue sky for a single cloud;
I see a gray possibility on the distant horizon.

The stone memorial stands upright in the corner;
a single poet sits under a willow writing.

Jimmy Pappas

Orange Sun

I drove to work and watched the orange sun
on the horizon just above the road ahead.

It had not yet risen, but there it was. Its rays
had bent around the Earth. My eyes saw straight.

The result was a sun which was not where it
appeared to be, in a color that was not what

it really was. So I stared as I rode along hoping
to catch that moment when it turned yellow.

It escaped me and left me to wonder about
how quickly a lie can blend into the truth.

NOIR
A libretto for a "concept album"

(HE)
There is always the woman, always the mystery that we will never solve.

I sat alone in my office waiting for the phone to ring. Slowly sipping a glass of Jamison. The shades were drawn. I was about to put my headphones on when there was a knock at the door.

Come in, it's open.

She entered. To say "goddess" would be entirely inappropriate but it brings you into the right area. Blond, unbelievably dressed. Her clothes both covered and uncovered her nervous, elegant, experienced body.

(HE)
Why did you come here?

(SHE)
I had nowhere else to go.

(HE, singing)
A woman comes into your life

The way a burst of weather comes
Snow, rain, and you have to deal with it
Sip your whiskey, listen for the warning drums

A woman enters your eyes
The way a tear finds its way to it
Hold tight to the deep surprise
Wonder, just wonder what to say to it

(SHE, singing)
A man gone to seed is what I see
A shabby man in a shabby place
Why ever did I come here
Was it a longing for disgrace

Was it a desire to be queen
In a kingdom made of dirt?
You've sampled men before
Your heart's been opened, hurt.

(HE)
What do you want?

(SHE)
I'm looking for my sister.

(HE)
How old is she?

(SHE)
Young. Twenty-three.

(HE)
When did you last see her?

(SHE)
A year ago, at her wedding.

(HE)
Where is her husband?

(SHE)
Gone, perhaps with her, perhaps not.

(HE)
You haven't heard from her.

(SHE)
Not a word.

(HE)
Why did you come to me?

(SHE)
I was told you would ask no questions if I gave you money.

(HE, SHE—singing, duet)
In the darkness of the city

I work with whatever I can get
The darkness hides things I don't ask about
So much of life is regret

So much of life is effort
To keep one step ahead of the funeral pyre
Four fifths of life is tedium
One fifth is fire.

One fifth is fire.

***

(SHE)
Daddy, I want you to meet Sam Argüelles. He's a private detective.

(HE)
They lived in a mansion straight out of the 1920s. Erich Von Stroheim
didn't rise from his chair. He seemed frail and old. Nasty. A thin arm
reached out to me.

(HE)
Yes, I am, sir. I understand you want me to find your daughter.

(DADDY)
PAH!
I want her to get rid of the fool she wed.
I want her back in her own sweet bed...

(singing)
I'm a rich old man
I made money
I made money
And money made me

I have two daughters
One's in my clutches
One's in my clutches
But the other ran free

The one in my clutches
She will lure you
Take you to her bed
Till she can't endure you

Then she'll come back
Ashamed and sorry
Telling her daddy
He needn't worry

She'll fool you with love
But your brows will lour
Cause love's not her game
Her game is power

She's daddy's daughter
M' own true love
She changes like water

Like the stars above
(HE/SHE echoing)
She's daddy's daughter
Your own true love
She changes like water
Like the stars above

(HE, aside)
But she's beautiful
And I'm in her power
I believe in love
And our love might flower

ALL THREE (SINGING TOGETHER)

(SHE)
He's the man for me
I'm in his power
I believe in love
And love might flower

(HE)
She's beautiful
And I'm in her power
I believe in love
And our love might flower

(DADDY)
She's daddy's daughter

M' own true love
She changes like water
Like the stars above

(DADDY spoken)
Do you still have your gun, sweetheart?

(SHE)
Yes.

(DADDY, cackling)
Good.
Maybe you'll shoot *me* sometime.

***

(HE)
I left before anyone shot anyone. Their words stayed with me as I looked for the lost daughter. Lost. The streets were busy and crowded. Bright sunshine in desolate LA. Was anybody happy, here or anywhere? I lived in Paradise—Paradise Lost. Daughter lost. Me the finder, more lost than anyone. Tell me your story. Tell me the history of those blue eyes. Call me Johnny Dollar.

I found her at a Travelodge on Pico Boulevard in Santa Monica. It wasn't hard. She registered in her husband's name. But he wasn't there. He was long gone.

(singing)

Where is your lover, baby,
Is he up in the air
I look all around
And he isn't there

Might be in Vegas
Might be in Malibu
Might be anywhere
Except with you

(DAUGHTER, singing)
I'm all alone
In a real tough town
People up
People down

Can't trust people
Though you want them too
Might be in Vegas
Or in Malibu

(DAUGHTER)
He drew all our money out of the bank. Told me he'd be back in an
hour. He wasn't.

(HE)
She was thinner than her sister. Wore glasses. The sister was the pretty
one. She was the one who read books.
They didn't prepare her.

(DAUGHTER)
Did daddy hire you?

(HE)
No, your sister. Your father wants you back.

(DAUGHTER)
Not till he's dead. I'll go back then.

(HE)
I have to tell him I found you. And where.

(SHE)
Give me twenty-four hours.

(HE)
I made my report, doing as she asked. The old man died about a year later, his missing daughter still missing. Died of natural causes. As for the beautiful daughter, we tried but it never worked out. She had too many problems. Daddy was her true love. I miss her as I write this. I think the old man killed her heart. The other daughter was maimed but managed to get away. My own heart is missing in this equation. It still beats, I'll give you that. One more loss in this city of Lost Angels. I'll tell you it doesn't matter. Are you interested in this story? One more casualty on the boulevard of broken dreams. Or we put it that way. There are other ways to put it. *So we beat on, boats against the current, borne back ceaselessly into the past.*

NOIR

Means the labyrinth of the city
        Means the labyrinth of the city
New York-San Francisco-Vienna-Berlin-LA
        New York-San Francisco-Vienna-Berlin-LA
Noir
        Noir
Is "post war"
        Is "post war"
During the war
        During the war
You had orders,
        You had orders,
However insane
        However insane
You had a structure
        You had a structure
Called "command"
        Called "command"
Now you are alone
        Now you are alone
With no one to give you
        With no one to give you
Orders
        Orders
But the dangers of war
        But the dangers of war
Are still with you
        Are still with you
During the war

During the war
You had a sergeant
    You had a sergeant
And a discernable enemy
    And a discernable enemy
You could hate
    You could hate
Now it is unclear, unclear
    Now it is unclear, unclear, unclear
Who your friend is
    Who your friend is
Who is your enemy
    Who is your enemy
Now the war
    Now the war
Seems to be within
    Seems to be within
You don't know
    You don't know
Betrayal is everywhere
    Betrayal is everywhere
You associate
    You associate
With the rich
    With the rich
But you understand
    But you understand
Their corruption
    Their corruption

And you both want
  And you both want
And don't want
  And don't want
Money
  Money

You carry a gun
  You carry a gun
For "protection"
  For "protection"
As you carried a weapon
  As you carried a weapon
During the war
  During the war
Noir
  Noir
Is that woman
  Is that woman
Whose allure you can't resist
  Whose allure you can't resist
But should resist
  But should resist
Because she too
  Because she too
May be your enemy
  May be your enemy
You may have to put her in jail

       You may have to put her in jail
Desire
       Desire
Flares up constantly
       Flares up constantly
But desire
       But desire
May be deadly
       May be deadly
This is noir
       This is noir
Darkness everywhere
       Darkness everywhere
Guns pointing at you
       *Guns pointing at yo*u
From the shadows
       From the shadows
You know they're there
       You know they're there
But you don't know who they are
       But you don't know who they are
Or why
       Or why
They wish to kill you.
       *They wish to kill yo*u.
Capitalism
       Capitalism
Has invented noir
       Has invented noir

Capitalism
  Capitalism
Is at the heart of its darkness
  Is at the heart of its darkness
COMPETITION
IS WAR

You spend your money
  You spend your money
You spend your life
  You spend your life
And the woman who loves you
  And the woman who loves you
Carries a gun
  Carries a gun
And is willing, like you,
  And is willing, like you,
To use it.
  To use it.

LAMIA

Take my breath
Take my heartbeat
Take my smile
Take my soul
But stay alive
You are so far
But I feel you close
You can't come back
But I know where you are
You can't say a word
But I can hear your voice
You can't send me flowers
But I know you smell mine
I don't know your address
But you know that
I'm sending you letters
I don't know your age now
But you know that IN MY HEART
You are immortal.

Warda Atroun

A dream inside a dream

It is that speechless song
And noisy silence
Of benighted angels.
A dream weaves a dream
Begets timeless images
Cuts into ugly hubs of moaning
As fast as clouds
Meeting sun beams.
They surrender virtuously.
A dream is the realm of infants
And newborns' untold stories.
A dream inside a dream
Is eternity within fate's lap
Cradled in a spacious orb
Like a blue pigeon catching light
From a sable-hideous night.
Children shall smile in dreams
And motherhood's inquiry to heaven
As sighs and letters of victory
Shall be heard as canons.

Incomplete

How many necklaces
Broken like my bones
One linked to another
When the sun is up
Torn and spread out
At night
Finally we realize
That we are incomplete
A stifling couple
Distance our future home
No meeting will gather us again
I lost a smile within your days
I see no happiness beaming
Let my wings swim
Beneath an entranced sky
Let me breath love
And believe that angels exist
Let me shape my dreams
And watch the sun
Rising in the west

George Held

Plane

Not "aero" or "hydro,"
just plain plane, with a near

handle like a saw's
and a knob in front

and a blade on the flat
underside; this tool,

held two-handed, you push
(or pull, the Japanese way)

across the edge of a piece
of wood to "plane"

it smooth and level
And then, maybe,

To add a bevel.

George Held

Homeless

As autumn makes its annual swerve
toward winter, the homeless

multiply on the streets like mice
in alleys, and the domiciled

shun them like carriers of measles
or other popular viruses.

Some homeless have belongings
stacked in shopping carts but most

wear their belongings on their backs
and spend cold nights in makeshift

dens of cardboard or discarded cloth
from refuse stacked for collection.

However much we resist the thought,
the homeless are our sisters and brothers,

and we the domiciled must avoid
the shun and the cringe and offer

them any assistance we can –
a dollar, a candy bar, a scarf –

without even reflecting that
there but for the grace of God,

or the finger of Fate, go I.
We are all, potentially,

homeless, uprooted, like Puerto
Ricans after Maria,

or worse off than the children
interned at the U.S. southern border.

George Held

Rectitude

< Rectus n. Latin: right, straight

You give us rectangles
and homo erectus
upright and rectum.
You erect the standard
for what is correct
and you correct us
when out of line.

Where are the upright pols,
like Lincoln or Truman,
when we need them?
Why are we ourselves
not sufficiently upright
not to need them?
Citizens, like arrows, must fly straight.

George Held

Not a Scientist

Though admittedly not a scientist, Trump
slits his eyes and loudly harrumphs,

"Climate change is no longer a hoax,
"but it could change back, no joke,

"and then we'd have egg on our face,
"with millions of jobs gone to waste.

"So let's wait and see for a while,"
he says, flashing a lunatic smile,

"and keep the economy strong –
"this warming, I know, won't last very long."

Donald Gasperson

standing goat mountain

there's rare clean air
above the timberline
and summer's melting snow

after ages of glaciation
in bone jarring quiet

a high alpine cirque
a neat stone garden
for tenacious vegetation

with a clarity of mind
to hear the beating
of your heart

tinnitus and old memories
the soles of your shoes
all have echoes of their own

a common reflection
on casual narcissism

blood pumping
good walking days
it's nature to forgive

a marmot whistles
alerting pica and all
to possible trespass

yet not a careless step
or scattering of rock
on standing goat mountain

Robert L. Penick

Your Future, Burning

It is the sixth of July and fireworks
are *Buy One Get Two Free* at the stand
in the Dollar General parking lot.
Ninety-six degrees Fahrenheit
and the cars crawl, armored ants,
to their destinations. Movement
and purpose. For one hundred years
society has had a lit fuse attached
to its overfed, all-consuming ass.
Now the buffets are failing,
mankind's muscle atrophying
into a gelatinous mass of
sloth and privilege. Turn up
the air conditioning, venture out
only at dawn and dusk, and pay
no attention to the acrid scent
of this world on fire.

Arleen Williams

Tree-Crook Nest

Her book tucked waist-tight in cut-off jeans
Monkey child scampers up the fir tower
To her tree-crook nest in a secret green world
Far from the other world, a world far below

A world in the making, a labor of love
With a dusty driveway to a hilltop home
With horsehead windows in red barn doors
And a white-railed riding ring with homemade jumps

A world of hungry cows and bony nags
Of failed gardens and too many chores
Where blackberry brambles, foxgloves and thistles
Steal over-grazed pasturelands, a farmer's folly

A world of Bonneville lines and Bonneville land
Where power lines mar Mount Rainier views
While grass grows lush on easement lands
Child-high grass for hungry cows and bony nags

Monkey child, long-limbed and string-bean skinny
Age six, nine, twelve, the middle of nine others
In need of ... what? Solitude, escape, self?
Scampers from nag's back to tree-crook nest
From horse hair to rough bark, from sweat to sap

105

Perched high in tree-green world, alone and free
Monkey child picks pitch from scraped elbows
Wipes hands, adjusts her glasses, and settles in to read

Arleen Williams

My Father's Daughter

I am my father's daughter
In my refusal to accept limitations
In myself, in others, in life
I hold my father's pride, his pain

Will I live to eighty?
Will I cycle? Will I write? Will I love through pain?
Like my father, hammer or welding torch in hand,
Until he could create no more?

Will I pull inward?
Will I limit my world? My words? My love?
Like my father with scars around his heart
Until he could love no more?

I push too hard and want too much,
I refuse life's limitations, I refuse my own
I struggle to love, to learn from life
I am my father's daughter. I am more.

diario xlix

a short poem about the showers sweet their death
in May the lovers' wont and clouds excel on pointed
reefs and heavens where no boneless god relieves
uneven number and spaceless boundaries the end
of all short poems the brief and weeping disconsolate
when recalling moments all too short the rains
that compelled the eye to turn and sleep that gave
the poem its brief and dreams of countless animals
of blind and young the thing working in the grass
the leafy shoots the sprouts and buds that lovers
embrace in their deluded guise and high above the
cloudless element the poem with its clay and subtlety
the legends spun the strings undone the colors bright
the hue and echo in each untrammeled verse a traffic
of fireflies and midges the nodding assent of death
the palace underneath the worms' abode that yawns
like an abyss for all the poem curtailed in its sweet
recall and endless rhymes in the mouths of bards
whose dying breath is legend in the leaf and green
as ever the new-born sun turning darker as noon
is won and grief the upper hand maintains while
light seeks refuge in the bane and all but hills
in shadowy disdain keep moving slowly to the end
this little poem about springtime's alert these words
fashioned from the sorrowing pen and the brain
itself in its sink and pan can but weep the memory

of one clad in the cloth of merciless childhood so
brief as is this poem for no one sung but loss

diario lvi
keeping in mind the oncoming rains the winds
the seeding and the new leafage and how green
must the horizon be for the dead in their floating
island a mansion a hotel a room with proper parts
and the wailing and remembering and flickering
to the southernmost isle the abode of the dead
candles can barely see two ells in front and to be sure
is that Joe on the extreme left and the ghostly sigh
a whisper betraying bodily torments exiguous
as the voice lost in the desert sands the smallest
the frailest recognition like a photograph blown up
and suddenly sent into remission to reappear
six decades later of Joe and his half leaning against
the invisible world a parapet of tumbling summers
vain automobile excursions to Hades and back
thick dense rope of water underneath no reflections
only miasma and dereliction and the contours
of the several months it takes to ripen death's holiday
a riot of song and immersion and nocturnal flight
the stars! verdant clusters of bright and shining
like burgeoning grapes held high in Bacchus' fist
everything is unseen and time is no greater than
the thumbnail of a friend disappearing in the dark
can their faces be so handsome so doomed to ruin?

in the ear the running and rushing of the years
no sense can be made of the metal where sleep
is manufactured nor of the boundaries of space
infinitesimal grass weaving through fingers
abstractions called art and history and enormous
conflagrations on the other side of the sun
blackening just as Joe is turning to soot and ash
except for the face captured by light and for a moment
only as vivid as still-life allows far from the truth
to the southernmost isle the abode of the dead
long nights together sewn within the lunar dream
wet peril of the Pleiades and house of Aquarius
and Zeus standing great in girt and height
shaking prepared to hurl his missile
will Augustus be pleased with this poem?

diario lxiii
(a)

what ends in the photograph is time
light captured ravished by shadows
masks that in space freeze their features
no sound alerts the chorus of winds
no green sprouts intrude their lusty growth
a footfall is all the song one can surmise
and brother and his peers all sweet
their hair a lyric upswept and languished
here come the undertakers in their leaf
and the verbiage of air and passing cloud
the riot of memory when the silent sea

is the other side of light if not the moon
with its marks of beautiful irregularity?
poem of the sun blackening in the heart
and planets invisible and unnamed that
took the shore with waves raining photons
what steam coursing through eyes held fast
their aim the unseen god who directs
with unerring dart their swift demise
outside the frame beyond the camera's pulse
the lens stained with keen foreboding
a day will come when fading all will fail
the bright of that summer hour the dense
shape of the unknown moving like a knife
through discourse and reason and smiles
and brittle throat celluloid reversed and smaller
still the imperceptible inch of reverie
the catch in the illusory index
when no number exists to realize time
in the chiaroscuro mausoleum of loss

(b)

hibiscus and rhododendron steep climbing
the light's false cliff you who was but one
among the trembling blooms your face a fuse
charged against diminishing time the high
and illusive idea of image impressed
like a thumb of ink upon vanishing air
a page or two scramble of sybilline sounds
interpretations of wind beating in the void
and sky's ever azure assumptions making

of *that* day the only one a leaf perfected
in its hue by the mind's undressed rhetoric
a vast a tomb a style a phrase broken
into figures multiple by two and dense
the grass dry in its bent hemisphere a lure
to flame and weed alike the rounded cavity
where thoughts go buried in miasma dark
to hold the pose and strike the brow with ice
like glass shatters all around the atmosphere
a holy once then fall down shoulder knee
and shadow convicted in the camera's eye

Thaddeus Rutkowski

GLASS AND TEARS

He was watching some television—
Christmas songs on a DVD—
and getting ready for bed,
when he dropped a glass.
It was a new glass; he wasn't attached to it.
But when it gave up its life,
he started to cry, not just for the glass,
but for everything else that was broken.

Those broken things came rushing at him
as he swept up the fragments,
knowing he would not spot them all.
He would find slivers of glass later,
when, with bare feet, he stepped on them.

Shin-Yu Pai

Having a kombucha with you

is even more fun than going to St. Petersburg, Beirut, or Berlin
or having a leaky gut on Las Ramblas in Barcelona,
partly because in your turquoise track jacket you resemble a bolder
version of the curator from the Larry Rivers painting,
partly because of my love for you, partly because of your love for
pumpkin pie at Thanksgiving, partly because of the pale pink sakura
blooms blanketing the streets, partly because of the surreptitious
quality our smiles take on before strangers and Asians,
it's hard to believe when I'm with you that there can be anything as
still,
as solemn, as unpleasantly definitive as chapels, when right in front of
one in the cold 7 o'clock light we flicker back and forth
between each other like a plastic fire fabricated by the faux Amish,
and the literary fair seems to lack all expression, you suddenly wonder
why in the world anyone ever put pen to paper.

I gaze at you and I would rather look at you than the Royal Arts of
Jodphur, except perhaps a Mughal prince on occasion and anyway,
Yale published the catalogue raisonné, which thank Buddha, you
haven't bought, though we could go to Toronto and the fact that you
drape yourself like a Roman when toweling off more or less takes care
of Mapplethorpe, just as at home I never think of the Futurists or
at a supper club a single painting by Van Gogh that used to make me
sob
and what good does all the study of a VFX animator do

114

when they never enter into the language of water, fire, or cloud,
or for that matter Winslow Homer's seas after he drafted Civil War
camps so crudely it seems they were all cheated of some marvelous
experience, which is not lost on me which is why I'm confessing to
you.

in the garden of Danny Woo*

I lead you up terraced slopes
until we see clear to Hing Hay Park

down Maynard Street, rattling
off the annals of Uncle Bob

how he leased the land
beneath our feet to feed

the elders, create
a thriving ecosystem where

there had only been neglect,
a plot of land covered in trash

& shattered glass restored to
life-giving beds of vegetables

through a shared belief in change,
fallen now into decay rain-soaked

winter leaves rotting underfoot,
the reports of sex trafficking

in massage parlors down the way
replete with unhappy endings,

you startle me from remoteness
when you pull me close, to quiet

speech, our tongues entwined in
some scattering of verdancy come alive

(This poem first appeared in the Seattle Review of Books)

Jazno Francoeur

Via Sacra

I was buried beside an olive tree
with a lamp, three figs, and a loaf of bread.
I was never a mother, nor a wife,
my duties conferred to the sacred flame
to attend the vestal hearth in winter,
to bless the Tiber's water with my palms,

and then relieve the burning in my palms.
The Sacred Way is just beyond this tree,
where my lovers visit every winter
to share my memory with leavened bread
and hold their blackened fingers to a flame.
I was never destined to be a wife

they knew they could not take me as a wife:
the random lots were held against my palms
and made my fingers curl into a flame
then open as a blossom on a tree.
My mother wept; my father gave me bread.
We walked to an empty house in winter

just beyond the Sacred Way in winter,
my dowry paid in full– not as a wife
but rather as a holy child, whose bread
had crumbled to ashes between her palms;

I watched him pass under the olive tree
bending low, as a hand cupped to a flame,

his body disappearing like a flame.
All the days of my twentieth winter
were marked through every season on this tree:
proscribed from vagaries of man and wife,
I rubbed its soothing oil between my palms
and gazed from windows when we made the bread,

when I crushed the grain into flour for bread.
I pressed bellows, bearing the oven's flame
to watch the bodies grow between my palms,
rising from dust, hardening in winter.
I was never destined to be a wife,
to be embraced by lovers near this tree

or kiss their palms, which hold the leavened bread
before an olive tree; or lift a flame
to see their winter eyes expect a wife.

Jazno Francouer

The Vow

We remitted my father this year to the nameless earth,
where no gods churn the ground with their invisible hands
and no resurrected form yet retains his strange acuity. We eulogized him
then went about our business, dazed for a time, then made a vow
to spread his ashes where he and his wife had left
their disparate passions. The business of the living is to return

the memories of the dead to a verbal corpus and to return
their myths to a physical place on the earth
and perhaps find some measure of comfort in what is left
after their ashes are wind-borne. My hands
tremble at this thought, the emptied vessel, the vow
to ascribe meaning to a meaningless death, to vow to forget in him

a terrible iniquity and thus a childhood lost: yet also to find in him
such boundless joy among the Aspen and evergreen, the return
to the garden, before the temptation and Adam's vow,
before he rose up from God's cruel breath and the earth,
before his own trembling hands
had limned the contours of his nakedness, and hers. All that is left

is this jar of desiccated dreams, all that is left
of my father is a thimbleful of questions.   I still see him
when I dream, driving an empty bus, his hands

curled about the door handle like Charon on his return
from the River Styx, ferrying me and my daughter from the earth
across the threshold.   Sometimes he vows

we will be safe on our journey; in other dreams, he vows
nothing, but is consigned to the end, rolling onto his left
side in silence like St. Lawrence on hot coals, the earth
finally collapsing in around him.
He was a martyr even among the living, and in return
we grieved at his every step downward, our hands

bound by his prophecy, knowing his hands
were summarily free to fashion his end. Yet I vow
that this is not his end, and that in these words he will return
if only for a moment from the edge of that darkling plain, where he left
Blake and Arnold to confer with him
under the shadow of the Earth.

This is my wish, to return his voice to the living; to feel his hands
once more upon my shoulder as I walk the earth, and to vow
this is not all that is left of him.

Hamish Todd

Looking for Sustenance

(For my mother)

I am digging clams
It's been a long time
Since when I was little
It is a gray day
By the ferry dock
South, or East
Towards the abandoned houses

I love this part of the beach
Reclaiming house pieces
Admiring special stones
But today
I'm looking for sustenance

The only clam I find
Is hiding poorly
Just under the sand
In a saltwater tide pool

Otherwise
The beach is too rocky to dig
I don't have a good shovel
I give up and go to Wedding Beach
Opting for blue mussels

That remind me of Scotland
By the moors
Perrins and after that
On Lewis
Picking them for supper
And bringing them home to mother
Hoping for a smile

Hamish Todd

Mine Eyes

It's my eyes
I'll miss the most
I've always enjoyed
The moon
Even when the stars
Aren't available
Due to too many humans
And their blasted lights

Be it crescent
Or full
Or somewhere in-between
Waxing and Waning
Pulling and pushing the tide
In clear weather
Cold or in the warmth
Of summer

It's these eyes
I'll miss the most
All they have fallen upon
Like a light snowfall
Has filled my memory banks
To the point now
Where instant recall

Is sometimes a thing
Of the past

As I will be before too long
And as I think of that
I think of things I'll miss
About this plain

Not the sense of touch,
Which is okay, but pales
In comparison to sight
Same goes for the ears,
Yes, they're handy companions
And make for good poems
Sometimes

My member has
Only ever
Gotten me into trouble
What started with the eyes
Lead me down those roads
Where all the senses were
Engaged the most

Eyes, not particularly attractive
Slightly color-blind but 20-20
Most of my life
Slipping a little now
But I can still drive and read

And see the sunrise
The redsets from the summer
Fires

My eyes have seen
The world's population double
And I am younger than some
I don't foretell
Nor do I regret
I only know the traffic
I won't miss at all

It's my eyes
That I'll miss the most
The shoreline and the coast
Father, Son, Holy Ghost
Take me any time now
I'm ready to come home

Julene Tripp Weaver

The Revival of the Blackwing Pencil

Have you used a pencil lately?
You may think, Pencil! That's old school.
But East of Eden was written in pencil.
That first draft when John Steinbeck
started each day with sixty Blackwing 602s
each used till too short for his hand.

Made by Fabor-Castell (Since 1761)—
when the factory closed it was a sad day.
Stephen Sondheim bought pencils by the case.

Grapes of Wrath was written in pen.
Now we have the revival—
the Blackwing limited edition
made to specificity, total black, even the eraser
as Steinbeck's son said his dad would prefer.
24 packed neat, with donations made

to fund music and art.
An inexpensive hobby to pursue, pencils:
We revise not erase the past.

Julene Tripp Weaver

Born Rusty

Born rusty with a long attached
noose—a cut cord we forever breathe
through—old already in our burdened
birth, wanting a rebirth at the very start
of our existence. That first gasping breath
the lights glare, the crawl to the teat for
sustenance. The claws

we develop as we grow in this
mess—born into a world we might have
otherwise ignored—how long this thread,
a constant nag like a knit sweater we can't
get right, coiled shaky fingers misjudged
when the earth shook beneath our feet
and our heart broken, tears expressed
inward for lack of comfort found. We
will our self each victory despite each
hardship, but will the tether truly ever
sever? Will the rusty indelible ink
in our fabric ever wash out? A gift

we learn to accept in the first
forward step leaving that last moment,
a way to gauge, a way to have a bigger
history then we ever expected, we learn

to sit with ourselves till the story ends,
to find the bright star, a guide, and we
follow, accept our rust, the bloody cut
that never heals because it is the entrance
the universe finds to heal us. And,

I didn't even get to sex. That fluid
wavelength that bends our DNA, moves
our center into constant motion, toward
conception where all begins again.

Pamela Carter

WE DREAM OF THE DEAD AND THEY ARE NOT DEAD

You emailed about your dream—
the old boyfriend
appears for casual conversation at the rural home
of our grandparents, but he is dead.
Killed himself some years ago.
Dream minds don't care about death.

We can talk to anyone
when we dream. And they are not
dirt-covered or ghostly or
the least bit decayed. They wear
khakis and button-downs and sandals
because they are in the countryside.

Their skin looks like our own browns
and pinks and they tell us no
special secrets about what lies beyond.
Then his head vaporizes.

Dead and headless old boyfriends sit,
like regular folk, in rattan chairs
in our dreams. Their heads reappear,
if we keep talking, and may look
more insect-y, big blinkless eyes
on stalks. Perhaps no mouth?

Through his metamorphoses
though, he remains himself. In my own dreams
I've heard my mother-in-law's voice, absent
from waking life more than a decade
and, the other night, hugged our grandfather
who died when I was in grad school.
Oh, sister, our dreams can be so good
to us, even if a little Dali-esque.
They say, *See, he is living still.*
See, he is forever in your cells.
Find him there whenever you sleep.

Pamela Carter

SOME OF US WILL NOT BE KING

let wind offer her speed to someone else

when sad we prefer to cry
unlike those throned

we will suck icicles
despite their dirtiness and cold
and tromp in our big boots
to flop into snowdrift-soft meadows
uncrowned

others can claim our thunder

others can churn our rivers

we wish instead to make happy the child
each of us knew
the child each of us was

we will be angels of the flake-crystal world

some of us will not be king

(This poem first appeared in the 2019 Poets on the Coast Anthology.)

Pamela Carter

AFTER READING PAULA MEEHAN

*I think the whole river of poetry is a history of the dream life and the
dreaming of the human species ... we can solve things through
dreaming, I think we can embed important memories, survival
strategies, through dreaming. It's the place where everybody is a poet,
in the dream.*

—Paula Meehan

the whole ocean of dream life
and dreaming
can solve things

in dreams we devise survival

in dreams we fashion floating
and dog paddle

in dreams we invent colors unavailable
when awake

winedark   ultragreen   infrapink

carry these pigments
in purse or pocket to draw upon

133

in case of emergency
or display
as proofs of infinities

or convince ourselves
of our own actual sizes

perhaps the crisis comes today

tuck last night's dream
in a convenient location

Rayn Roberts

Eagle Bowl

In warm air I grow, a weed in a dry field by a stadium

nothing much sprouts where I am
I suck up all the water where only a lizard may live,
in spring a few wildflowers may color the space
summer consumes in high heat

The soil so rocky not worth a worm's ass
trampled by thousands of feet
when people fill the bowl with screams
songs in the tribal rites of autumn.

It's been centuries since the tzoailli, idols of god.

Gardeners pull me out by the root, call me pigweed
farmers hate me, make bonfires of me.
When men come with the pigskin, they do not eat me
people offer popcorn, hotdogs, beer, blood, war

not in the old way, in an odd way, it satisfies Huitzilopochtl.

Ellen Reimschussel

One Nation Under Heavy Fire

We watch puzzled as the abused returns to the abuser,
the votes come in,
the court fails to convict,
the building crumbles
under heavy fire.

"We dove for the dugout,
those of us who were on the field"

What does it mean to love a person, a nation, a God
of our own making?
the man you thought he was,
the shining city on a melting patchwork quilt.
the one who chose you, above everyone else,
to be special.

"And, what ran through my mind was, 'Why
would anybody be trying to shoot
birds at six o'clock in the morning'"

Under heavy fire, I dreamed I mattered.
So lucky to be born in the right country,
in the right religion, the right color.

"But there was gunfire going overhead, so I couldn't get out there"

How easy to disavow the diseased limb,
as though it sprang from a different trunk,
as though our roots don't clutch bloody soil,
as though the bullets overhead aren't American made?

"When you've got a baseball bat and the guy's got a rifle"

All I want is to believe
we can heal something broken
from conception.
All I need is to pretend our fathers
didn't own people,
there was a time things were better,
I am not culpable,
someone else will fix it.

"Then there was silence, I thought it was over"

(Quotes are from witnesses of June 14, 2017 Congressional Baseball Shooting)

Redshift

They say even the void holds no peace:
thinning. My days thin. We who cannot
kill ourselves only
grow past humanity. That,
the mechanical burden of shouting, this,
the repetition of blood flow.
The universe will not implode only grow past meaning.
Oh how I love you some moments.
In the beginning we feared the beginning
would be the end. In the middle, that we would
be the end. In the end, that there would be no end.
Only the horrible thinning. I know once,
we ate cereal around a breakfast table,
twilight through the windows:
a vegetable garden, a swing set,
mountains eating half the sky.

Ellen Reimschussel

(untitled)

Spring came too early this year,
the branches spiked with pink, This, the warmest
February on record. Red and yellow construction
cranes sprout from every corner.
The city's heart races. Lake Union bristles
with light; the iridescent coats of crows pockmark
the shore. Your favorite color.
We watch Queen Anne hill
drill out of the earth, threaded
with glinting white boxes.
You take my hand.
Everything is wrong and beautiful.

HILL TIPPING *

the first stage of the life cycle is hibernation
my back against your full belly
colonies die off not because of the cold, but for a lack of food
I am dressed not for warmth, but for closeness

occasionally, emerging queens will stray into living quarters
my love for you is quite apparent here
contrary to popular belief, cold harsh winters are actually good for
wasp populations
which comes in waves of relief

queens stay asleep until plants start to flower, and there is ample
nectar to support them

queens will hibernate in crevices and sheltered places
I write to the rhythm of your sleeping breath
the progeny come together in a mating swarm. when this happens on a
hill,
kochikochi, kachikochi of the clock's hands
the mating wasps are seen rolling down the hill and this is known as
hill tipping
I wait for morning, the pair of young does, who brave us for
outstretched apples

(excerpts collaged from a commercial website for WaspBane in Godmanchester, Cambridgeshire)

Catherine Renyolds

THE PARIS OF YOUR ARMS

This early, I am
seemingly made up of cities
a balcony to take in first air.
Street cleaners and patisserie stands,
checkered tables

I come with a dog-eared suitcase,
I arrive at your lips prepared
for travel, a half-cocked smile
at your disarrayed dresser
forted with half-burnt candles, socks
traversing the length of bedroom.

Half-awake, I ask to be fed olives one
by one, divide your past by two.
That's how long you say ghosts last.
Put your lips to my heart, like Neruda insists.
Let your fingers strike
bargains beneath me.

Catherine Reynolds

DEER POINT

August,
I held onto you like a small stone
as we drove along turtleback mountains
rising up from sudden coast.
Slow turns of madrona and churchyard,
fences sagged with lilac—
a wild blue body.

We drove past the trusting stands
of ripe berries in anticipation
of one another, the darkness of farms
the yellow barge of moon parting
banks between us.

And as we crossed over that last river
before turning onto the highway, you told me
of an island once visited as a child,
the deer tamed by apples–
How you could reach out a hand
and feed them sweetness,
their rough tongues leaving salt rivers.

Just then, you put your mouth to
mine and offered me the same.
How I wanted to be fruit passed

salt to seed, seed to lip
spread out on those field overturned with earth.

A speck on the wall

I don't want to be a fly. My mother told Brad, her boyfriend of nearly the entire time I was a teenager, that it was time they cooled off and maybe thought long and hard about what it meant for them to be together. You talked to Kathy, he said. I have thoughts of my own, and even if I did talk to Kathy, she is my own flesh and blood and I'm likely to take her council concerning something as serious as this. She filled you with ideas. I have my own concepts, my own direction, and it is precisely this sort of accusation that has produced in me a lingering addiction to Maker's Mark and a strident aversion to hearing you ascribe to me my own motives and interior thought processes, because despite your claims otherwise, Brad, you have never been able to read my mind. You drink too much. I drink too much because of you and your smell and if I'm drunk enough, I can ignore that stench of animal musk you bath in and the little song you are always humming under your breath softly enough that you think that no one notices it, but I notice, and I can tell that it is the "The Ocean" by Zeppelin and for your information, Brad, no one except fourteen-year-olds in 1984 listen to Zeppelin. Are you drunk now? I'm fortified with my conviction to see that you pack your things tonight and take your Oldsmobile and your RV to the trailer park where you belong. I pay rent on this dump. I own the roof on this place even if the bank owns the foundation, and it passed the inspection and would be a home if you had not turned it into a prison, but as the owner of these four walls I can dismiss the warden. How drunk are you? I'm leaning into my freedom and will have you take your portable prison with you and you can set those four walls across town. You've had a psychotic break. I'm breaking with the psychotic, if that is what you mean.

Brad packed his things into his three suitcases and drove away in his Oldsmobile. My mom and I lived in the shadow of his RV for three days. In the darkness when the moon set, I could hear it spit and groan and the beige box covered in streamers of sea moss eased out into the dark cul-de-sac. I wish I had been a speck on the wall when she said what she said. Because I don't want to be a fly.

Bethany Reid

Years before Her Death

Through fields bright with dust and Canadian thistle,
we rode our horses to the creek. At the back
of the farm, ancient alders and hemlock fir
stood like caryatids, holding up the sky.
The horses waded to their bellies,
plunging their noses where the pull of the creek
was greatest. I looped my stirrups
over the saddle horn to keep them dry.
My cousin unfastened her hair,
cupped a hand to the dark, mirroring water,
and lifted it to her lips. This is the dream
of my childhood. All night I have reined
my bay horse back to that still place. All night
I have watched her reflection waver and beckon.

The Grief Eaters

The day we buried her, a light mist fell,
the damp at the graveside just enough
to make us button our coats.
At the hall, later, we unbuttoned
and peeled off our coats, told stories
and laughed, as if we'd left our grief
piled in damp mounds in another room.
When rain ruined the harvest, summers
of my childhood, my father, hating to waste it,
put it in the barn anyway,
and we'd lose a cow or two that winter
to bellyache. The day we buried her,
we put up our grief exactly like that,
knowing it would later have to be eaten.

Bethany Reid

The Crossing

The last calf of the last spring
of my father's life,
it stood bawling, stuck on the far side
of the pond's green circle.
From the porch, we watched through cracked panes
to see what it would do.
A bull calf, a Hereford, so fresh
on the earth, white face and red body
still tufted where its dam had licked
the afterbirth away.
The pond wasn't deep,
except with April's muck and rushes,
the bursting of buttercups,
polliwogs poised in their jelly
like fruit waiting in apple blossoms.
The calf braced itself
against all persuasion, head down
and legs splayed, its voice a steady bellow
like a bell tolling.
A few months later, we were astonished
at how quickly my father
crossed from this life
to the next, how he splashed
through the mucky divide, years
falling away behind him, burdens

he would no longer carry.
This last decade while my mother declined
and lingered, I often felt Dad's presence,
long-suffering, close by.
Last night didn't I dream of that calf,
his legs stockinged in pond muck,
as he trotted up the hill after his kind?
In my dream, two figures, buttressed together
and lowing, waited in a circle
of verdant light and called my name.

Keith Holyoak

Gettysburg

Fourth of July, blue lookouts hold their posts
On Cemetery Ridge. Much has changed
The past three days—above, young rebel ghosts
Lament; below, cannon have rearranged
Limbs of men and horses. Summer rains
Cleanse the field of slave power, bugles sound
Freedom rising. Those who forged the chains,
Or broke them, take their quarrel underground.

On Decoration Day the children place
Lilies and lilacs on the soldiers' graves;
Rolling down grassy mounds from monuments
They play together, smiles of every race.
Beneath the Copse of Trees a father waves—
A change has come, a moment's innocence.

Keith Holyoak

Confluence

Two streams converge, one blue, one brown.
The first is freshly melted snow—
Straight from the mountain it pours down.
The other's spent some time below.

Alike in width, and depth, and force
They flow a distance side by side,
As if content to share the course
With neither crossing their divide.

But fingers touch, and changes follow.
Blue turns gold—though not so pure,
The richer color seems less shallow
And glistens with its own allure;

Nor is the mingling just one-sided—
Harsh brown takes on a softer sheen,
As though it's willing to be guided
Back to what it once had been.

Most of a mile one might suppose
Fresh innocence dilutes old sins,
Until downstream the river shows
How in the end, mud always wins.

Keith Holyoak

Moon Over Green Lake

Horses—unsaddled, flanks brushed dry of sweat,
Back from a trail threading through pine and aspen—
They, and their riders, sense the day complete,
The hour come round to let the cougar pass in
Places their own spoor has been newly set.
While creatures dream in stable and in cabin
I lie awake because a heartsick loon
Wailed from a ladder hanging from the moon.

I rise and walk out on a rough-hewn float
That answers to my footfall, trembling, swaying,
The full moon swaying, clear as abstract thought,
Its light like summer snowflakes falling, dying
Into the waters, near and yet remote—
Poised on the edge I stare through ripples, weighing
Whether to climb the ladder or to swim
Down where the moon dissolves, its light gone dim.

Sometimes that moon of long ago still rises
In my eyes, reflecting on Green Lake;
Viewed through its luminance the world's disguises
Melt away—the frantic crowds, the fake
Friendships for sale, the hyped-up plastic prizes
Are gone, gone are the fraudsters on the take—
I ride through clover all the afternoon
And in the evening hear the heartsick loon.

Crow Convention

Local news mentioned crows,
  how they gather from time to time,
  from miles around, all in one tree for a night or two, and
  then disperse to their individual neighborhoods…
  how it was happening near a local campus, and
  drawing big crowds of onlookers.
Told my partner about it, and so she and I went
  to see the crow convention out east of town,
  watching from the top deck of a parking garage
  as thousands of crows flew in from all directions.
They filled a big tree, numerous as leaves
  but more crows were arriving, and
  the tree became overcrowded.
So the crows left that tree in a cawing, flapping stampede,
  to circle more, argue some more, which tree tp try,
  flew all around the neighborhood trying to decide
  on just the right tree.
You know how conventions sometimes amount to nothing much,
  except shuffling and scuffling and a lot of loud talk,
  well, crows do it too.
So… no sound decision happened and they flew round and round
  till dark, then they all disappeared, perhaps
  into the bar next door for socializing, or
  into one another's motel rooms.
The breeze was way too cold to just stand around

in the parking garage so we found a comfortable looking tree
for spending the night, then climbed in and
flicked on the TV to see the congressional hearings about
what to do next, but nobody talked straight.
So we shut it off, climbed back down and joined the crows
over at the bar.
Sometimes conventions, like congress, don't amount to much.
but like the crows, a whole murder of politicians
can be fun to watch,
as they flap and caw, circling around,
accomplishing nothing other than
production of guano.

N'Orleans, Winter, 1958

Like my wizened great aunt Myrtle
Who used to play boogie boogie piano
In questionable late night venues,
That old hotel room had seen it all…
That room didn't give a *damn* that I'd
Hitched all the way from Los Angeles for
Just a thin blanket and cold lumpy bed.

The desk clerk's wrinkled clothes
Sported evidence of his supper when
He stood to pocket my money, then
Tossed my key onto the counter and
Sat back down facing the TV.
Black and white it was, and upstairs,
My room's broken window allowed
Just a few vagrant snowflakes.

Never saw snow any other of my
Times in N'Orleans. In the morning
No sign of snow, just a dirty street
Leading to a seedy restaurant, and
My "eggs over easy" hard-cooked.

HARD COOKED! What kind of a

Half-assed place…? Walked out,
Caught a ride out of town, north,
New York City…. Nothing there for me.
Bussride to East Orange, New Jersey, then
Headed home, hitching all the way until,

Let out just before Ohio River bridge,
Wheeling, West Virginia, night time
Walking, crossing bridge, howling cold wind,
Hands freezing, no grip, dropped suitcase.

Dropped suitcase! Opened it right there,
Got socks, put them on for mittens and
Once across river, looked all around
Till I found greyhound station,
Last money… ticket… candy bar.
A few coins left over, stinkin' dirty,
Slept through Ohio, to Muncie,
A dime for city bus, and finally,
Home… knocked the door and
Mom asked, "are you hungry?"

Thomas Hubbard

Indigenous Thanksgiving

(for the rest of us)
Paint your face black today, cousins.
Black in mourning for a lost world,
>   for a culture wounded and bleeding,
>   for wounds of ancestors who tried to ward off invaders,
>   for africans enslaved by rich americans,
>   for blackened rubble in the arab lands.

Paint rushmore black today, cousins.
Black for the huge lies those four politicians told.

Paint the day black, cousins.
Black because it so closely follows the day invaders call "columbus day."

Paint the damned turkey black, cousins.
Black for self-righteous words
>   words about "let no child be hungry thanksgiving day,"
>   what about all the other days?
>   words about "free thanksgiving lunch for the homeless,"
>   what about the days before or after?
>   words about "thankful to be living in a free country,"
>   what about those who don't feel free?
>   words about "such a beautiful land we live in,"
>   what about pollution, junkyards, climate change?

Better yet, forget the turkey
turn away from the pumpkin pie
shun the shopping malls

Instead, tell old stories to the kids, and
honor your ancestors.

Sheikha A.

Maktoob

Starvation is a lost rhythm of invention:
they tear out of webs of light like nuance

between warm and cold; they transliterate
the codes of artificial darkness as absence

of utility. If I tell you what a camel's hump
stores, you will slice through it with a palate

of giving to its mysteries for mere sake of
taste. We are taught to dream *halal*:

believe in our visions sent by the universe
a pack of wings floating as gossamer

parachutes that serve a *nur* expelled
from orbital lamps. My mother dreams

of green chickens parading a courtyard
led by a yellow peacock. I tell her this

could mean wealth or calamitous belligerence,
the order unspecific, for we give ourselves

to hunger daily like untimely prayers;
for we know the air in our bellies as salvation;

160

the tone of tears that have dried wells
of progeny; she tries to remember the cry

of molten steel. Instead, she deduces
green is the colour of spiritual harvest,

and holds grains of dead crops in her palm
like combustion. Dark drapes its *burqa'a*.

We slip behind projections of prophecies
I tell her could mean nothing. We have

tendered a raging maw with hysterical
sleep. Tonight will be of modest dreams.

Sheikha A.

Galaxy

after Starry Starry Night, painting by Tighe O' Donoghue Ross

The hour is early in the night: 23.23;   the sands of the Sahara
have lifted with the breeze like a million swirling galaxies.

He uprooted a date palm with hands bare as his unclothed
back, calloused from cupping shadows like handful of water;

it was easier to build from an elk's horns — the antlers mapping
the nodes from east to west — a canoe of coarse base, panning

the width of a calm sea, and an owl placed on its tail for fortune;
soon, the sky would huddle its frame and the stars would align

in parallel circles, like streets if it were atop a boulevard
of pruned homes glowing like bulbs of fireflies; and the man

in the Sahara with back as bare as his dreams about the sea,
charting the nautical weight of his flesh, as white as the bones

of his illusions, where he isn't alone, and the date palm he tore
out of the sand erected at the elk's hip, notorious as his burdens,

scaling the untameable sails blooming like a stalk of a flower—
kingdom waiting by a horizon not yet lowered to his gaze. The sky

flows waveless on water, golden as the fleece on the night's back:
as elk as the emblem on its chest, humming to the stars to cast

themselves into the sand, cause it to shimmer, so he rests
where it is home: desert and sea spilling into a sparkling oasis.

James Eret

Death at the Kabul Marketplace

I awoke to the wails of the muezzin
From the minaret. On the mountains,
Layers of fog masked the fir forests.

I awoke to the calls from the horn of plenty,
Seeds planted in my memory.
Today's sun shines on market day.

Forgetting the fire and fear of those slayers
Of my sleep, my sons and daughters,
I haggled for fruits and fares.

Arcing from the mountains came produce
No one bargained for, let loose
From the mists that always hide a truce.

I awoke, hearing shrapnel burst and fly
Around me like a mad festival, the brooding
Mountain peaks silently soaking up

More of the feuding history of my blood.
I awoke and haggled for fruit and my life and lost.

James Eret

Chisel

"Who will walk with me into this terrible and beautiful world?"
—Dorrianne Laux

Looking down from the rocky fortresses, the imposing parapets,
In the crystal Valletta Harbor, the dghajsas, the bum-boats we called them,
Moored together in families of primary colors,
Sun-saturated and joyful bobbing,
Laid-back lifestyle of Malta.

That eyeball staring at the sun too long,
Slashed with blood and veined
8-Ball hemorrhage.

The sailor, lone sentinel swiveled on the bar stool,
Knew we saw his eye but said nothing;
But so much anger burned in his eye.

Just how did you get that eye?

The White Mice, the Shore Patrol, did this to me.
At Mail Call I got a Dear John letter from my girlfriend.

He ascended the elevator from Hell

To the Garden of Hesperides,
Where the lovers strolled, hand in hand, made out,
Surrounded by the olive trees,
Those benevolent branches,
A quietus in King's Cross,
The sounds in the distance
Of prayers and chanting Latin vespers.

So filled with good tidings he approached the precipice.
The idea was to finish his leap,
To die in Valletta, Malta,
Such an exotic and mysterious country.

The White Mice talked him down,
No ordinary drunk poised on the edge of the cliff,
His mistake to start cursing them back.

They did it with their night sticks,
While straightjacketed on a litter—
He told the White Mice to fuck themselves
And they thumped and thumped
Blunt trauma bloat his evil eye.

Blind Homer, strumming your sad lyre, sing those songs,
That smell of lemons and olive trees, sea- surge of distant lovers,
Never again to walk, hand in hand.

Crysta Casey

Harborview Custodian, Burn Unit

I wore scrubs, sterile booties,
and gloves, a mask over mouth
and nose. I discard one set of booties
and gloves when I left one room
and put on another set for the next room.
I yielded my mop as I had been taught
in the classes preparing me for this job:
side to side goes the mop
like a woman lightly tossing her wet head
of gray hair. I was afraid of the mop
tangling with an intravenous pole
as if in a drunken brawl,
knocking the pole over and the needle out
of the burn victim's arm.

I scrub the dead skin
from bathroom stalls,
from the big tubs they soaked in,
from the mirrors where they didn't know
the monsters looking back at themselves.
Some were in airtight plastic
cubicles from outer space, lying
naked – they wouldn't make it.

Then, alone, I entered a room.
A toddler with burns on his arms
and face, stood in his crib
and screamed with open arms,
wanting to be touched.
And I couldn't touch him.

(Reprinted from Chrysanthemum Anthology 2006, with permission
from The Estate of Crysta Casey)

Jerry Austin

Trailhead Sign at Wallace Falls

There is something unnatural
in the world —

Something godlessly wrong –
as I read the sign

That at night
the waterfall closes; the access,

The trail to it,
closes. And I imagine

And remember at night
with fellow campers

Happy as owls
if a bit spooked, as we camped —

Legally — from camp Huston
below — up near the falls

In these Sasquatch
woods, and the myth-sized

Log that dreamed
beside me as I dreamed

Of fern and moss and forgotten
trees that somewhere still

In their circles, gathered
like old stones.

In the nearest distance
splashed the death-beautiful

Death-powerful falls, and
we, the children,

Where the waters
brightened the stone,

Slept in that green singing
and woke to the first song.

Five Tanka

in static cold
the ex-soldier interprets
falling snow
as the gauze like mask
his heroin was

years later
her sunflowers
still alive
laughing at the sun
still not trusting stars

children in cages
have become the norm
their days highlight
is standing in uncramped halls
while the rooms are cleaned

with no more faith
than I had when I entered
I leave the church
to bury another friend
who'd want a drink now

I miss the loons
and their sharp cries
almost quaint now
as I lay in bed counting
the gunshots outside

Christine Tabaka

Going Away

I will not go away,
not for long.
The sparrow has not
finished singing her song.

Eyes of the black moon,
covered by night.
A path of sparse means
closes too soon.

A journey from nowhere
starts where it ends.
A gift given in regret
looking for atonement.

I shall remain
where I need to be.
There is no turning back.
The sparrow has flown away.

Christine Tabaka

Entrenched

I have become too much of what I am.
Delved too much into my own transgressions.

Escape is no longer possible,
as wholeness eludes me.

The center has pulled away from its core,
It dangles frayed with disillusion.

An eternity of self-imposed blindness
leaves scars that will not mend.

I stand naked before myself,
seeking absolution.

I cannot see beyond my own
desperate minute of existence.

I have become too much of who I am.
I am the goblet of regret.

Christine Tabaka

The Weary and the Strong

There are two kinds of people
with slight distinctions in motif,
ones who are driven forth and thrive,
and those who barely subsist.

Some toil with tireless energy
feeding off an endorphin high.
Others prefer to stand idly by,
only doing what is required.

As if a cruel trick
upon mankind was played,
these two usually end up paired.
As an old saying goes "opposites attract."

I was once strong, but ebbed,
waning into the low reaches of doubt.
Do I get a chance to redo
what I have duly discarded?

A matter of 'nature or nurture.'
A question of who or why?
The black versus white,
and fate versus fact.

Are these traits woven within us,
or do we thrust them upon ourselves?
Are we born to go forth and conquer,
or is it something that we choose?

The weary and the strong,
side by side march along.
There is reason nor rhyme in both,
and the world continues to spin.

MaryEllen Talley

Dear Fire —
    after Susan Rich

You conspire against
the very edge of charring.
Here the empty fireplace
with its iron grill
and open flue.
We place an array of narrow kindling
in crosshatch pattern

(the cool checkerboard of evening)

tuck crumpled newspaper into spaces
add smaller wood
and light the match to watch paper shrivel
            red then black,
wait while burn takes hold —
we make our moves
to angle on one log and then another —
large enough
to make time slow
as many pages turning.

Just when the burning light is strong
we lift and align the largest logs
to make a splendid blaze in captured time,

sit with tea and brie and bread,
mindful when flames ebb
and we move to add another log
        until we are consumed
in this blue-walled reading reverie —
the rapid burn of soft cedar,
crackle of spruce,
our one-upmanship of wood.
We let the fire fade —
spread ebony cinders
into flickering afterglow.

Sandra Evans Falconer

The Dazzle of Beads

My bathroom looks the same
as you saw it last.
The dogwood branch, sprayed white,
festooned with its earrings & bright beads,
the rocks arranged on the sink,
a lavender sea fan
netting a pair of miniature pointe shoes.
'Where's the john?" Mother
used to joke,
looking for simple porcelain,
ordinary spigots at the sink.
You used to drag friends
clear across the living room
to the place where I prepare myself
to face the world outside.

I rise daily to that world,
with memories of another:
Dad walking barefoot down the hall
searching my bathroom in vain
for a comb;
Peter's homemade sign
hanging on the door:
"This room is condemned
by the Board of Health,"

and then you —
so taken by my harmless pageantry,
the only one who
stopped by to see the whimsy
and clearly cherished it,
loved all of me,
down to the last brilliant bead.

("Dazzle of Beads" first appeared in *The Baltimore City Paper* in 2002)

Sandra Evans Falconer

Hearts, Held

For a gift one Christmas
I bought Steven miniature chocolates,
each one wrapped in pictures
of playing cards:
The Queen of Hearts,
the Jack of Clubs.
For years every Yuletide he kept them
in a cut glass bowl.
I knew the chocolate inside
had to be brittle,
probably bitter.
Perhaps he hadn't liked the taste,
or never tried one.
The chocolates became
like the unwrapped soap in his bathroom,
the fish forks, still shiny,
above the sink:
these small gifts, pleasures
somehow synonymous with guilt.
Luxuries dealt like cards,
a good hand never played,
but held in tight,
close to the heart.

("Hearts Held" first appeared in *The Baltimore Review, 2008)*

Distinguish

Thousands of drifting
children beg
on the street
and thousands are *of*
>the street: thousands of children
>drifting outside mosques and market stalls.

It's hard to tell
the child *on* the street
>who returns to a family at night
>to share her earnings—
from the child *of* the street
who sleeps wherever she can,
>enduring kicks by men evicting
>her from storefront steps.

And what about that girl
no longer a child? The one no one
>sees at night. The one who
>drifts alone on shadowed
streets, to sell her young body
to buy food for her family
>in a faraway village.

Tell me, which child's hand most deserves
>your hard-earned coins?

Ann Hursey

I See an Old Woman Gardening

in the rain at my favorite community garden,
and park by the curb to see what others grow in June:
Plots thick with radish, peas, and arugula. Eager rows
of starts preparing for warmer August days.

By the tallest of the raised beds, high
enough for those who cannot bend or kneel,
an old woman pulls her weeds and mutters. We talk
over the slow drizzle, how everything loves to grow.
She speaks in a clear foreign accent. I ask her
where she is from and she explains everything:

Finnish widow of seven years, cancer
survivor of four. Today she plants red onions,
squishes slugs with woodchips, or thumbs—
anything handy. Sprinkles slug bait
on her organic garden; winks—
calls it *cornmeal.* She tells me her husband
visits her in dreams. Tells her to *move*
to some retirement condo—so she won't
have to work so hard.

She shakes her head, incredulous—
and asks him, *but what shall we eat?*

Karin Ancellin

Interview with the Moon

…….

Yes! I have, more than once in my life
suffered the pangs of lack of light,
my albedo not quite right
dark thoughts lurking
though I'm not good at emoting

………

my childhood was seldom joy filled
as my father's rays came to me befuddled
my mother, the earth, had so much on her own
that she could not have my needs be known
So I pouted and looked the other way

………..

Not at all, I don't do it on purpose
the tides follow my trajectory, I don't impose,
it's just gravity, I'm only Selene, the sun my master
allays my orbit, his is twice greater
than my inordinate responsibility

………

Not to this day, but I see the useless satellites
every day, whether I'm there or out of sight,
piles of junk orbit with and around me.
What is to happen to all these debris?

When my proxy life ends,

......

yours will dim, dark.

Karin Ancellin

gmail-novel

To Eliza

Persephone wrote a novel, but it's not published yet.
Thousands of love letters, her romance while it lasted.

A zealous exchange, at least six emails each day
they didn't even need each other's flesh, as they were writing away,
but words wore out. All meanings and connotations experimented,
the concept had waned. It had to be ended.

re: so she left the computer, trying to recompose her being
the addiction had enslaved her routine
her early waking eyes sleep-walked to the screen
words, impossible to erase, as easy as it seemed.

re: hours she had met with the machine,
sitting, and, typing, and, sighing, and, correcting
each keyboard-letter, emerged of its own accord
laughing its way to the email frame, never bored!

re: the comfortable desk chair now sat cold
no more fuming teacups spilled on the desk, hands old
wasted as if she came out of AA, or of a night in central park
the sun had gone out, the keyboard had gone black.

re: all these words lost in the ether, immaterial ideas
imprisoned in the intensity of their letters' follies
she printed them, pale dead bodies without a casket
then shredded them into fine strips, score for a foregone minuet

re: the epic conversation still lies on the server of a heartless
corporation
warden of the love data, awaiting i-cloud destruction
So she took the strips, assembled them on a canvas
created two fluttering white wings, dotted in small black print animas.

When I Walk Your Property

Just beneath Bald Mountain and your crooked
chimney with chipping mortar, the faded
cedar shakes hold strong against summer
storms and cold snows. Although you lived
here alone, they're not your shakes though,
the home having been rebuilt long ago on
the same stone foundation which once
formed your basement.

I wonder what you kept down there,
What you stored on your shelves-
Jars of preserves? Squash and root vegetables?
Stories or photographs no one will ever see?

I try to feel the cold of walking back from your
outhouse on a January night, a dozen paces guided
through falling snowflakes by the flickering flame
of an oil lamp, still sleepy but stunned by winter's
bite into wakefulness, and then the stinging warmth
of opening the woodstove door to feed the
fire, before returning to an empty bed.

While you remain faceless, I imagine you plucking
the first few apples, ripe and red, from the trees
you'd hope to harvest from for years to come,

see you planting the hydrangeas edging your porch,
young and leggy paniculatas packed with potential.
Now unpruned and neglected, suckers shoot up to
the sky weighing down the unshapely shrubs with
an inferno of bright blossoms, while peonies and
hostas beg for division, but bloom where they can.

Black bear and turkey now call home to the forests
that have reclaimed your fields and I find myself
curious over so much-

     What did you keep for animals?
     Were any with you when you went?
     Were any left outside and what became of them?
     Who was your closest neighbor, and how long
     was it before they knew?

So many strong women who choose to
live alone are ostracized.

     How were you?
     Did you move here like we did —
     to get away?

I'm glad someone named our road after you so
that we can wander and wonder over your
story, your road where old barbed wire fences
still run parallel through the hearts of oaks
and birches you knew only as babies.

Josh Nicolaisen

Our Stuff

Grandpa Chet's skillet still fries eggs,
his shelves still hold books.

Uncle Mark's walking stick still stands
straight, still goes for walks, his
poles still fish the Isles of Shoals.

Aunt Julie's Yahtzee dice still roll
near a crystal candy dish still full
of peppermints and toffee, a dish from
Denmark— my great-great grandparents'.

Just today Great Grandpa Nic's spade
dug and divided a hearty row of hosta
while a pile of weaker, broken shovel
blades builds beside our barn,

and I thought about what my
things might do someday,
without me.

Mary M. Sesso

Red Noise

It's the sound of the sun turning
dark and a blood moon spilling
over the earth,
a red light in a window filling
the room with promises of delight,
the taste of regret on a cheater's
tongue after a hot, one-night stand,
the stain of sin on Mephistopheles'
gaudy red shirt and tights as he leads
Faust off stage into hell,
the color of guilt on Cain's bloody
hands after killing Abel
and the haze hovering above a rose
in a stem vase on the white table
which together play like a symphony.

The Apple Orchard

It begins like this:
sometime after dark
the deer show up
silent as flurrying snow
to eat the sour, wormy
apples lying in the icy mud.

I watch from the window—
The moon licks away
their color, leaving them
bone-pale, almost silvery.
I felt like I am the center
of the universe where deer
the color of the moon
move quiet as drifting
blossoms just to please me.

Too soon darkness takes over
and I retreat into winter
where hooves striking
the ground are forbidden,
where the quiet is endless

John W. Gorski

A Parisian Couple (after Courbet)

She remembers his hands
framing the pensive face
that returns her gaze now
in the lamplit mirror she holds.
In a gas lit café on the Rue de Seine
last month, she listened to the wine—
driven babble of his bohemian verse
and the narcotic plaint of the Voyage
to that perfumed isle in the Aegean.
She looks for spider-gray strands
in her hair but finds none;
she inspects for wrinkles
that don't appear in her face
softly brimming with the new moon.
Where did he go? She wonders.
He said Marseilles, she recalls.
Her reflected eyes turn sea-green.

He strolls along a beach in the south
of France in a beige summer suit.
His mind laughs aloud
with the opium verses of Baudelaire.
Suddenly, he waves his hat in the air
toward an invisible vessel in the distance
as he stands near warm shallows at Palavas.

Under a sun-bleached lilac sky,
his thoughts are scattered
and his pockets, penniless.
He has squandered his fare
to the mystical island on absinthe.
He looks out on waters growing darker
until the horizon is stopped
by a margin of lamp black.
Her scent of jasmine and rose
arrives upon the breeze,
as in her Paris quarters, she regards
the void of her unanswered letters
and the absent side of the bed.

Men with Too Much Time on Their Hands

Unacclaimed Artist

A cupboard is opened to reveal a hidden room
where a bald, aged man sits at an empty canvass studying
the absence of his dreams. By his side is a cup of espresso to caffeinate
the isolation of his day to day. He doesn't paint much anymore,
having given up on achieving the transcendent liquid blue
of Mt. Fuji he had seen flowing in a book of contemporary art.
He slumps in his chair as he regards some of his half finished
work gathering dust on easels in this studio in the house of his nephew
who is a patron of his lost cause. The light through a side window
comes in filled with the singing and laughter of children that
turns the neighborhood into the ancient chant: "ashes, ashes,
we all fall down." Sometimes, he has encountered them with their
ADHD screams as they scampered away from him on the sidewalk.
Now, evening filters into the pallor of his room and he waits
for the night to arrive dark as black coffee.

When I Lived Among Norwegians

My fiftyish neighbor used to watch me park my car
those years I rented a one-bedroom on 17th NW. In the summer
I would happen upon a man in his sixties – wearing an old undershirt –
as he sat on a chair in front of a discount barbershop on 15th Avenue
and watched the cars pass in gray Ballard light to Market Street.

Outside the post office, a long-haired man with a Civil War beard
would try to teach his dog to dance to "Highway to Hell"
blaring from his second-hand boom box. Now that I think about it:
none of these men seemed to have a meaningful hobby.

Fear of Old

Fifteen years ago, me and my brother and his wife went to the Norse
Home one day to arrange a residency in assisted living for our mother.
Noticing the brass forest of horns clamoring Big Band music from a
stereo
down the hall my sister-in-law opined, "I guess by the time we live
here we'll be
hearing Jimi Hendrix." Warily, I envisioned purple haze edging a far
horizon in feedback.

KZOK

On Monday morning, I sit in my car listening to song after song on the
station
that is seemingly all Led Zeppelin at times. In the distance, a sea gull
cries
out in Jimmy Page chords. I am too retired.

ss

Stephen Roxborough

the oldest man in the world

relinquished his title
today

his neighbor said he was exhausted
from all the paparazzi
& tabloid reporters

his best friend said the gravity
of the situation caught up
with him

his grandson said the title meant
nothing to him
this was a perfect day
to let it go

most who knew him understood
the title was fleeting
a dream within a dream

everyone realized it was
about time

Stephen Roxborough

she noticed melancholia on the menu

at breakfast it was usually
between the juice & french toast

for lunch it often appeared
as a special side dish

when featured as a dinner entree
most of the kitchen staff

lost interest in customers
chefs stirred in detached circles

took up smoking & disappeared
on aimless meandering breaks

many others found their way
to the dark bar next door

slumped in a quiet corner
watching ice cubes melt

into the lonely bottom
of an empty rock glass

Esther Helfgott

Jamal Khashoggi

I think of him in the kitchen
when I'm stirring soup
or chopping
stubborn vegetables.

I think of him
as I turn the pages
of my book.

When I'm in the dentist's chair,
I hear him screaming
as they cut his fingers off.

I think of him
when I'm driving home
and at night when I'm writing
in my journal.

I think of him in my sleep.
I feel him in my chest.
He lives there.

Esther Helfgott

The Sound of Your Voice

> — for Raul, who speaks in silence

I wish you
would speak
your son's name
(*Keshava Kumara Sanchez*)
aloud, so everyone
could hear the sound of your voice (in grief)
I wish you could enunciate
each of the vowels that make up *Keshava's* name —
bring them into the world for us to hear.
I know this is too hard for you to do —
your son's breath has been in transit
for all these twenty years —
but I ask this of you anyway
so you will know
your grief
does not go unnoticed
by those
who savor the sound
of remembrance
and telling.

I want to know *Keshava's* story
though who am I to ask you to tell it —
a beautiful boy standing by the water's edge,

you write.

You say you speak his name in silence
but we hear you
across the vastness of grief
and the ocean of love.

Julie A. Dickson

Green Chairs *[for Donald Hall]*

1.

In a time when families came from farms,
my mother was born at home, with her
grandmother attending, standing by
to boil water and wrap a newborn
in soft blankets by the kitchen fire.
Donald Hall wrote of his family farm;
in his youth — he likely did not know
that one day his poems would incite
The New Yorker to publish his work

2.

ranging over many years of verse,
of non-fiction accounts of his life,
poetry written by him and Jane,
his student who loved and wrote poems,
who tragically died before her time.
He told and retold of his journey
through a marriage and children, divorced —
floundering through an alcohol haze,
falling in love, only to lose her —

3.

too soon she was taken, leaving him
alone once again, yet decades passed

before he grieved to full extent, he
wrote of this, reminiscing their life,
daily routine of long walks, writing
each morning close to Ragged Mountain
in his family's farmhouse with green chairs,
set on an open porch, rocking chairs,
the imprinted seats of ancestors .

4.

My father's family farm, in a town
near enough to my mother's — they did
not meet there, but nearby at the lake,
Ontario cottages owned by
respective family aunts, young teenaged
neighbors canoed and swam alongside
rocky shore, blue-green algae coated
boulders too slippery to climb on;
they often jumped off the public pier

5.

into icy-cold water, refreshed
after chores were done: hay in the loft,
cows milked, water toughs filled from metal
pails; they were allowed time at the lake.
Donald Hall wrote Ox-Cart Man, about
survival and hard work, known by most
farmers and families in rural
communities, who knew no diff'rent

other than livestock and crops growing

6.
to sustain their families, excess
brought to market, goods purchased in kind
helped to maintain their economy.
My father's farm grew asparagus,
his uncle overseeing acres
while in a garden nearby, two chairs
and table – machined metal painted green,
that my father kept with him after
leaving home then repainting them white,

7.
and finally green again at the last.
Hall wrote of Kurt, of Merz and baseball,
idols like Babe Ruth and Ted Williams,
players long dead, remembered ball games,
pitchers and catchers propelled the sport
from idyllic radio broadcasts
to farm families who could not see
players round bases, nor attend games,
but loved baseball heroes all the same.

8.
Did Hall know that he would be honored,
published and exalted, a poet
lauded as a U.S. Laureate,
author who loved solitude in youth,

prep school and college, honing his craft?
His great love lost, isolated to
recount life in verse, storyteller
of Eagle Pond, a family home
where words emerged in grand scale, floated

9.
to the surface, alliterative
algae on the pond, fodder to feed
a muse, hungry to embrace the past,
wrought with anguish and loss, as artist
he drew us into his world, the farm
loved by two poets stretched out before
his readers, budding poets who write
of simpler times, their memories and
perhaps muse on Hall's green farmhouse chairs.

Julie A. Dickson

Second Chance Child

Father of my being,
father I never met,
left for parts unknown,
drove on a change of wind,
away like scattered leaves,
far from forest home
to the south, grand plan
left behind a family
that ceased to exist
before ever becoming;
no cherished voices
sounded in his life,
barren existence,
he'd made his choice.

Second chance child
abandoned to fate,
childless couple's home
from legal arms eager,
to safety kept at arm's length,
pseudo-family embrace,
theirs not lacking gifts
of learning and hope
for life otherwise lost.

Contributors' Notes

Sheikha A. is from Pakistan and United Arab Emirates. Her work appears in a variety of literary venues, both print and online, including several anthologies by different presses. She has co-authored a short poetry collection entitled *Nyctophiliac Confessions* published by Praxis. Other recent publications include *Strange Horizons, Atlantean Publishing, Pedestal Magazine* and elsewhere.

Karine Leno Ancellin was born and grew up in New York City until she moved to live and visit different countries, from the Sahara region to Shanghai and Mumbai. She worked on 'Hybrid identities' for her PhD at the Vrije Universiteit of Brussels. She is now a professor, writer and translator living in Athens, Greece.

Ivan Arguelles is an American innovative poet. He received the Poetry Society of America's William Carlos Williams Award in 1989 as well as the Before Columbus Foundation's American Book Award in 2010. Goldfish Press published his recent book *Hoil* in 2019.

Warda Atroun is an Algerian poet and a multilingual writer and translator. She published her first poems in French at age 14. She authored her first book of poems at age 25 in Arabic. She is currently an educator and a teacher of foreign languages.

Jerry Austin is the editor and publisher of the new *Bellowing Ark Journal* and Press in Seattle, WA. He is literary consultant for this anthology.

207

Wendy Beamish was born in Vancouver, British Columbia, and for most of her life lived here. Educated at the University of British Columbia, she has taught English, Journalism and Creative Writing, as well as Media Arts. Wendy enjoys poetry because of the concise way it reveals powerful emotions that we all share.

Luis Berriozabal, born in Mexico, lives in Southern California, and works in the mental health field in Los Ángeles. His most recent poems have been published in Ariel Chart, Blue Collar Review, Piker ress, San Antonio Review, and Yellow Mama Magazine.

James Bertolino's career in poetry is long and distinguished. He has taught literature and creative writing for 36 years at Cornel, University of Cincinnati among other higher institutions. He recently edited *Last Call,* the anthology of Beer, Wine, and Spirits poetry. His most recent chapbook is *Galaxy in Thrall* from Goldfish Press. He lives with his wife, artist and poet Anita Boyle, on five acres near Bellingham.

Katherine Grace Bond writes to seek new conversations about the rifts in our psyches and culture. She is the author of *Summer of No Regrets* (Sourcebooks) and six other books of poetry and prose. Katherine offers an intensive year-long coaching program to novelists, memoirists and poets.

Matt Briggs is the author of *The Remains of River Names* and *Shoot the Buffalo*. His work has recently appeared in *The Kentucky Review, StringTown Magazine*, and *Cascadia Rising Review*. You can find him online at: suburgian.com.

John Burgess grew up in upstate New York, worked on a survey crew in Montana, taught English in Japan, and since 1985 has lived and worked in Seattle. He has written six books of poetry, including *These Streets*, a collaboration with his nephew J. Edward Moss.

Pamela Hobart Carter's poems have appeared in *Barrow Street, Pif, and The Seattle Star,* among others. From her Seattle home she also writes plays, fiction, and non-fiction, and enjoys heading into the Cascades to hike and ski.

Crysta Casey's information is available at www.crystacasey.com.

Yuan Changming published monographs on translation before leaving China. With a Canadian PhD in English, Yuan currently edits *Poetry Pacific* with Allen Yuan in Vancouver. Credits include ten Pushcart nominations, eight chapbooks & publications in *Best of the Best Canadian Poetry (2008-17)* & *BestNewPoemsOnline,* among 1,639 others across 44 countries.

Nominated for the Oregon Music Hall of Fame, SP Clarke has been a successful musician and music writer for forty years. A columnist and critic, he has more than one million words in print on the subject of Oregon music.

Lyn Coffin has published over a dozen books of poetry, including *Human Trappings* (1980), *The Poetry of Wickedness* (1981), *Crystals of the Unforeseen* (1999), and *Joseph* include the *Anthology of Georgian Poetry* (2013), edited by Dodona

Kiziria; and *White Picture* (2011), selected poems by Jiri Orten translated from the Czech.

Joanna Conom was born into the gray mist of Seattle and continues to reside there. Poetry was a love of her young life that was lost in the fog of adulthood. In 2011 during an acupuncture treatment Dr. Wu inserted needle in the top of her head and freed her poems. She has been writing ever since.

Julie A. Dickson is a poet in NH. Her work addresses abuse, animal captivity (especially elephants), environment and nature. Dickson was nominated in 2018 for a Push Cart prize, her work appears in Harvard Press, Blue Heron Review, Ekphrastic Review, Touchstone, Page & Spine, among other journals and on Amazon.

Mike Dillon lives in Indianola, Washington, a small town on Puget Sound northwest of Seattle. His most recent book is "Departures: Poetry and Prose on the Removal of Bainbridge Island's Japanese Americans After Pearl Harbor," from Unsolicited Press (2019).

Diana Elser was born in Montana; raised in west Texas and Utah; earned an English degree from Utah State. She raised four children in the Bay Area and Seattle and practices poetry via classes at Hugo House in Seattle, the annual Jackson Hole Writers Conference, and various online groups and classes.

Sandra Evans Falconer is an award-winning writer, poet, author and playwright. She is a recipient of an Individual Artists Award in Poetry from the Maryland State Arts Council, as well as an author of two poetry chapbooks and a full-length collection, *The Six o'clock Siren*. Her poems have been adapted for the Washington DC Playwrights Festival, and also set to music for an original song cycle for soprano Melissa Perry. Sandra's new book of poems, *The Lucky Spot Dance*, is forthcoming in the Spring of 2020 from Goldfish Press.

David Fewster is the author of *Diary of a Homeless Alcoholic Suicidal Maniac & Other Picture Postcards* (Tacoma Arts Commission, 2003). He also appears in the anthologies *Revival: Spoken Word from Lollapalooza 94* (Manic D Press) and *Thus Spake the Corpse Vol 2: An Exquisite Corpse Reader* (Black Sparrow Press, 2000).

Jack Foley has published16 poetry books, 5 books of criticism, a book of stories, and a 1300-page "chronoencyclopedia" of California poetry, *Visions & Affiliations*. Latest book: *When Sleep Comes: Shillelagh Songs. Jack Foley's Unmanageable Masterpiece*—a book about *Visions & Affiliations* edited by Dana Gioia—has also recently appeared.

Jazno Francoeur studied poetry at the University of Tennessee in 1987, and later mentored with Rush Rankin at the Kansas City Art Institute. His first book of blank verse, *Fountain Street*, was published in 2000 by Nettle Media. Jazno has continued to write formal verse since 2003, particularly sonnets, sonnet cycles, villanelles, and sestinas.

Donald E. Gasperson has earned a Master of Arts degree in Clinical Psychology and with a lifetime of reading, and simple persistence, words and writing came easily. The process of cultivating tip of the tongue experiences into a nuanced writing was remarkable and satisfying. He has had poetry published by *Quail Bell Magazine, Tipton Poetry Review* and *Bitch'n Kitsch*, among others.

John Gorski has lived in Seattle since 1976. He has also lived in Maryland and Ohio. He has a B.A. in English (University of Cincinnati). His poems have appeared in *Poetry On Buses* (2014), *Switched-On-Gutenberg* and *Five Willows Literary Review*. His latest book is *November Adrenaline* (Goldfish Press).

Winner of the 2019 blue ribbon for haiku at the NY State Fair on Long Island, George Held is a long-time poet and writer, with eleven Pushcart Prize nominations. His work has appeared in *Chrysanthemum, Five Willows, Spring*, and *Two Cities Review*, among other periodicals. He lives in NYC.

Esther Altshul Helfgott is the author of *Listening to Mozart: Poems of Alzheimer's* (Cave Moon Press, 2014); *Dear Alzheimer's: A Caregiver's Diary & Poems* (Cave Moon Press, 2013); *The Homeless One: A Poem in Many Voices* (Kota Press, 2000); and co-editor of *So, Dear Writer... An It's About Time Writers' Reading Series Anthology* (Cave Moon Press, 2019).

Michael G Hickey is widely published and has won numerous awards for writing, teaching, and union activism. He has taught creative writing at South Seattle College for 25 years, and in 2009 was elected Seattle's eighth "Poet Populist." He has volunteered as a writing instructor at prisons, juvenile detention, and bereavement camps for children. His motto is to "work hard and have fun." His life goal is to take over the world 25 students at a time.

Keith Holyoak was raised on a dairy farm in British Columbia, Canada. He is now a Distinguished Professor of Psychology at the University of California, Los Angeles, and a member of the American Academy of Arts and Sciences. He has published a volume of translations from classical Chinese poetry, as well as four volumes of his own original poetry.

Ann Batchelor Hursey's poems have appeared on Seattle buses, in *the Seattle Review, Raven Chronicles, and Crab Creek Review,* among others. Besides collaborating with a variety of artists, she has written poems to compost and hand-made-things. Her chapbook, *A Certain Hold*, was published by Finishing Line Press, 2014.

Thomas Jones began writing poetry when he was sixteen and wrote all through college. His favorite authors were Dylan Thomas, Shelley, ee cummings, Silvia Plath, Auden and the Beat Poets. He has had poems published in local newspapers and three books: Vantage Press/NYC called *Four Poets/100 Poems*, *Hour of The Poet/Thoughts Upon the Lake of Time*/Goldfish Publishing/Seattle Washington, *The Falling Light of Inspiration*/Amazon.

Born in Jersey City, raised in Los Angeles, Joel Kabakov was educated at UC Berkeley in music composition, Kabakov went on to a Graduate Prize Fellowship at Harvard and doctoral studies under Leon Kirchner and Leonard Bernstein. While in Cambridge MA, his poetical tendencies were catalyzed by encounters with master poets Octavio Paz and Robert Lowell. But not until year 2000 and a move to Seattle did Kabakov take his writing public. *Available Light* is Kabakov's book of collected poems published in 2015 by Goldfish Press, which was glowingly reviewed by *Harvard Colloquy.*

Mary Anna Kruch is a career educator and writer, inspired by her Italian family, PTSD, and nature. Recent poetry appears in *Five Willows Literary Review, Ariel Chart, Trinity Review, Wayne Literary Review,* and two anthologies. Her first poetry collection, *We Draw Breath from the Same Sky,* was published in 2019.

Sigrun Susan Lane has been fascinated by sea creatures since she was a child. She began her beach combing adventures from her childhood home in the Ballard neighborhood of Seattle. Now she walks the beaches of Harstine Island near her summer home. She lives in Seattle with her husband. She is the author of two chapbooks from Goldfish Press.

Lily Maltz writes, "Hi! My name is Lily Maltz, I am currently a sophomore at Hillside Student Community School. I love to ski, draw, read, and tinker. I am passionate about emergency medicine and someday would like to become an emergency room physician."

Rodger Martins's new book, *For All the Tea in ZhŌngguó,* was released in 2019. It follows *The Battlefield Guide*, (Hobblebush Books: 2010, 2013) and the selection of *The Blue Moon Series*, (Hobblebush Books: 2007) by *Small Press Review* which was one of its bi-monthly picks of the year. He is a New Hampshire State Council on the Arts in Education roster artist and also a touring artist for the New England States Touring Foundation administered by the New England Foundation for the Arts. He has also received an *Appalachia* award for poetry, a New Hampshire State Council on the Arts award for fiction, fellowships from The National Endowment for the Humanities to study T.S. Eliot and Thomas Hardy at Oxford University and John Milton at Duquesne University. His work has been published in literary journals and anthologies throughout the United States and China where he also wrote a series of essays on American poetry for *The Yangtze River Journal.*

David M. Mason is a retired research mathematician.

Joneve McCormick hosts and co-hosts several online poetry journals and her work has been published in various journals, periodicals and anthologies. *Three Poets: Voices from the West Coast,* an ebook which features the poetry of Koon Kau Woon and Changing Yuan, along with Joneve's, is available on Amazon. Two solo collections have been published: *The Visitor* (2019), and *Small Bird Bones* (chapbook, The New Press, NYC).

Bob Moore has been writing poetry and songs since the early 1990's. He's released several books of poetry his latest by Beech River Books entitled *Body and Soul* in 2018. Moore has also released several recordings including a collection of songs entitled *A Place to Start* in November of 2018. Moore is a regular at a writer's retreat held on Star Island off the coast of New Hampshire held annually the second weekend in September.

J. Edward Moss is a multi-media artist based out of Rochester, NY. He has published 3 of his works including his most recent collaboration

These Streets with his uncle John Burgess. This is his first time being featured in an anthology.

Joseph Musso lives in NJ, where he works with elderly dementia patients. His books include *I Was Never Cool, Red Somehow, Apartment Building, and The Cats Were Skinny but Cool About It.* He plays guitar, immerses himself in cinema, and loves to read books translated from all over the world.

Paul E Nelson founded SPLAB & the Cascadia Poetry Festival, wrote: *A Time Before Slaughter, American Sentences & American Prophets* (Interviews 1994-2012) is Co-Editor of *Make It True: Poetry from Cascadia, Samthology: Tribute to Sam Hamill, 56 Days of August: Poetry Postcards* & *Make It True meets Medusario.*

Josh Nicolaisen has taught English in both public and private schools for more than ten years. His poems have recently appeared or are forthcoming in *So It Goes, Tiny Seed Literary Journal, Writers Resist, The Poets of New England: Volume 1* (Underground Writers Association), and Indolent Books' online project, *What Rough Beast.*

Sandra Noel works as an illustrator developing award-winning interpretive signs. Her poems have appeared in *Pontoon, Buddhist Poetry Review, Elohi Gadugi Journal* and others. Chapbooks include, *The Gypsy in my Kitchen,* and *Into the Green,* Finishing Line Press, *The River,* Kelsay Press and *Unraveling the Endless Knot,* Middle Creek Publishing.

Shin Yu Pai is the author of many books, including *Aux Arcs, Adamantine, Works on Paper,* and *Sightings: Selected Works.* In March 2020, *ENSO* – a 20-year survey of her work across disciplines was published by Entre Rios. She earned her MFA from the School of the Art Institute of Chicago.

Jimmy Pappas served during the Vietnam War as an English language instructor training South Vietnamese soldiers. He is a retired teacher whose poems have been published in over 70 journals, including *Sheila Na-Gig, Shot Glass Journal, Off the Coast, Boston* So*Literary Magazine,* and *War, Literature and the Arts.* His poem "Bobby's Story" about the life of a Vietnam veteran won the *Rattle* 2018 Readers Choice Award. It is contained in his full-length book of war-related poems *Scream Wounds* (A15 Press, 2019). His chapbook *Falling off the Empire State Building* was selected as a winner of the *Rattle* Chapbook Contest and will be published in March 2020.

The poetry and prose of Robert L. Penick have appeared in over 100 different literary journals, including *The Hudson Review, North American Review,* and *The California Quarterly.* In 2018, he won the Slipstream Press chapbook competition.

Bethany Reid's two most recent books are *Sparrow*, which won the 2012 Gell Poetry Prize, and *Body My House* (2018), published by Seattle's Goldfish Press. Her poems have appeared in several anthologies, including the recent northwest favorite, *For the Love of Orcas*, as well as many print and on-line journals. Since retiring from full-time teaching, Bethany has been at work on a novel, and has

217

traveled to San Francisco, France, and Ireland to share her poems. She lives and writes in Edmonds, Washington.

Ellen Reimschussel has a degree in creative writing from Utah State University and is editorial assistant for this Chrysanthemum 2020 Literary Anthology.

Catherine Reynolds received her M.F.A. from Naropa University. Her work has appeared in *Sulfur, Ploughshares, Quarterly West* and she was the recipient of a 1999 Artist Trust Literature Fellowship. She has been a writer-in-residence through the Writers in the Schools program.

Rayn Roberts says, "I'm more a puppeteer than a poet. I dangle figures on stage to share insights and poke fun. I don't expect to enlighten anyone, but it could happen." He toured Ireland and England in 2018, where he was invited to read for the Dylan Thomas House by Geoff Haden in Swansea, Wales.

Liam Roche grew up seventh of nine in a big entertainment family that moved around a lot—coast to coast. His work is often inspired by his Catholic upbringing, naturalist/spiritualist take – spiced with a bit of psychedelia. At a young age, he was exposed to writers, artists, actors, and probably criminals that were part of the bohemian circle his parents drew in the 60s and 70s. He currently works as Systems Engineer in the computer industry.

Margaret Roncone's work has appeared in *Chysanthemum*, and on-line in *Barnwood International Poetry Journal, Avocet and Poets Against War*. Her poetry was performed as part of Pierce College 10-minute

Play Festival and was chosen to take part in Seattle City Council's Wordsworth program. She curated an open mic in Seattle for 10 years and also was facilitator for a poetry series at Chief Seattle Club. She currently lives on Vashon island where frequent forest walks and bus rides keep her inspired.

Stephen Roxborough is a dual-citizen Gemini, four-time Pushcart Prize nominee. His recent titles include *Ego to Earthschool* (2017), *The DNA of NHL* (2017). Editor and Creative Director of Neopoieis Press, Roxborough is currently finishing up books about New York, Amerika, and Impermanence.

Thaddeus Rutkowski is the author of six books. His novel *Haywire* won the Asian American Writers' Workshop's members' choice award, and his memoir *Guess and Check* won the Electronic Literature bronze award for multicultural fiction. He received a fiction writing fellowship from the New York Foundation for the Arts.

Marjorie Sadin is a nationally published poet with poems in such magazines as *The Little Magazine, Blaze Vox, Big Windows Review*, and the *Jewish Women's Literary Annual.* She has five books of poems in print including a full length book, *Vision of Lucha,* about struggle and survival, love, death, and family. Recently, Marjorie published a new chapbook, *Struck by Love.*

Leopoldo Seguel has hosted monthly readings at PoetryBridge at C&P Coffee in West Seattle for ten years featuring poets, storytellers and a community mic. His creative interest includes poetry, piano, collages, mobiles, small sculptures and co-creating artistic spaces. Leopoldo embraces art as a creative gateway to building robust and healthy communities.

Mary M. Sesso is a retired nurse who volunteers at the National Children's Center where she sits on the Human Rights Committee. Her latest work has been, or will, appear in *Comstock Revie, Helen Literary Magazine, Medical Literary Messenger and the Lock Raven Review*. Her chapbook, *The Open Window*, was published last year.

Ann Christine Tabaka was nominated for the 2017 Pushcart Prize in Poetry, has been internationally published, and won poetry awards from numerous publications. She is the author of 9 poetry books. Christine lives in Delaware.

Mary Ellen Talley's poems have been widely published in publications including *Raven Chronicles, Flatbush Review, and Banshee*, as well as in several poetry anthologies including *All We Can Hold and Ice Cream Poems*. Her poems have received two Pushcart nominations.

Hamish Todd was born in Liverpool, England. He came to the US with his mother at age 7. The Beatles music has always been a source of inspiration. He started writing poetry when he was 20. Mr. Todd went on to found two spoken word series and three newspapers, one of which was very successful: The Vashon Ticket had 10,000 readers and published for 7 plus years.

Rp Verlaine lives and writes in New York City. He has an MFA in creative writing from City College. He taught in New York Public schools for many years. No longer teaching, he continues to write and do photography in New York. He had a volume of poetry, *Damaged by Dames & Drinking,* published in 2017 and another, *Femme Fatales Movie Starlets & Rockers,* in 2018.

Julene Tripp Weaver, a native New Yorker, is a psychotherapist and writer in Seattle. Her book, t*ruth be bold—Serenading Life & Death in the Age of AIDS*, was a finalist for a *Lambda Literary Award,* and won the *Bisexual Book Award.*

Arleen Williams is an aspiring poet and author of three memoirs: *The Thirty-Ninth Victim, Mom's Last Move,* and *The Ex-Mexican Wives Club* as well as three novels: *Running Secrets, Biking Uphill,* and *Walking Home.* She is also the co-author of a dozen short books in easy English for adults. Arleen lives in Seattle and teaches at South Seattle College where she has worked with immigrants and refugees for over three decades.

&&&

Made in the USA
Middletown, DE
20 March 2022

62863134R00139